STOCKS AND FLOWS:
CARBON INVENTORY AND MITIGATION POTENTIAL
OF THE RUSSIAN FOREST AND LAND BASE

Brent Sohngen
Kenneth Andrasko
Mikhail Gytarsky
George Korovin
Lars Laestadius
Brian Murray
Anatoly Utkin
Dmitri Zamolodchikov

This report is a synthesis of a broader technical report, published originally in Russian as Zamolodchikov D.G., Korovin G.N., Utkin A.I., Chestnykh O.V., Sohngen B. 2005. *"Uglerod v lesnom fonde i selskohozyaistvennykh ugodyah Rossii [Carbon in forest and agricultural lands of Russia]."* Moscow, KMK Scientific Press Ltd. The English translation was done by Will Terrin with contributions from Volha Roshchanka. Both this report and the longer technical reports are available from the cooperating organizations' Web sites:

WRI: http://pubs.wri.org
FEPC: http://forest.cepl.rssi.ru
RTI: http://www.rti.org

WORLD
RESOURCES
INSTITUTE

Washington, DC

SHARON BARRELL
EDITOR

JUDITH CANNADA
LAYOUT

HYACINTH BILLINGS
PUBLICATIONS DIRECTOR

MAGGIE POWELL
COVER LAYOUT

Each World Resources Institute report represents a timely, scholarly treatment of a subject of public concern. WRI takes responsibility for choosing the study topics and guaranteeing its authors and researchers freedom of inquiry. It also solicits and responds to the guidance of advisory panels and expert reviewers. Unless otherwise stated, however, all the interpretation and findings set forth in WRI publications are those of the authors.

ISBN 1-56973-602-2

Cover photograph credit: Brent Sohngen
Printed in the United States on paper with 15% recycled content.

Table of Contents

List of Tables, Figures, and Boxes

Tables

Figures

Boxes

Acknowledgments

The authors would like to thank the following individuals for providing insightful comments on this publication: Richard Birdsey, U.S. Forest Service; Andrey Filipchuk, Deputy Director at All-Russian Research Institute for Silviculture and Mechanization in Forestry; Alexey Kokorin, World Wildlife Fund–Russia; and Roger Sedjo, Resources for the Future. At the U.S. Environmental Protection Agency, the publication was reviewed by Ben DeAngelo, Francisco De la Chesnaye, Dina Kruger, and Steven Rose. At World Resources Institute, Rob Bradley, Florence Daviet, Fran Irwin, and Janet Ranganathan made substantive comments during the early review of the publication, while Gayle Coolidge shepherded the publication through the review process. David Jhirad gave invaluable guidance throughout the creation of this document. Volha Roshchanka coordinated the production of this publication since its inception and facilitated its review and design. We also express our gratitude to Sharon Barrell, Maggie Powell, and Hyacinth Billings for assistance with editing and design.

While recognizing the contributions of those mentioned above, the authors alone are responsible for the views and perspectives expressed in this publication.

This work was supported by the U.S. Environmental Protection Agency, Office of Atmospheric Programs, through World Resources Institute under Cooperative Agreement No. X-82914501, and through RTI International under Contract No. GS-10F-0283K, and managed by Kenneth Andrasko.

Disclaimer: The views and opinions of the authors herein do not necessarily state or reflect those of the United States government or the U.S. Environmental Protection Agency.

Executive Summary

F orests within the Russian Federation are a critical component of the global carbon cycle. These forests are estimated to contain approximately 776 million hectares of forestland, or nearly 21 percent of the world's total, and store 289.4 (±71.8) billion tonnes of carbon, or 28 percent of global carbon, in above- and below-ground components. Historically, however, policy makers and scientists outside of Russia have had little access to data and information on the forest resources of Russia. Such data are vitally important for meeting the reporting requirements of the United Nations Framework Convention on Climate Change (UNFCCC) and for assessing the potential of Russia's forests and land use practices to enhance carbon storage above the levels expected to occur. Until now, few studies have investigated the economic potential for additional sequestration within the Russian Federation.

This report examines a number of issues related to forestry and forest carbon sequestration in the Russian Federation. It summarizes and synthesizes data and analytical results presented in a broader technical report developed by a team of Russian scientists (Zamolodchikov et al., 2005). The report is written for the international climate policy community, members of the Russian Federation government responsible for national reporting of forest carbon sinks, and members of the scientific community seeking a synthesized version of the longer technical report. The report's primary purpose is to address and answer three questions highlighted below.

1. **What is the status of Russian forestry data for assessing carbon stocks and flows and for conducting analysis of carbon sequestration potential?**

The results of our analysis suggest that Russia collects substantial data that can be used to estimate carbon fluxes (changes in carbon stocks) from forests. Ground-based inventories are used on 62 percent of forestland, and remotely sensed data have been used on an additional 31 percent of forestland. The data derived from these sources can be employed to estimate important variables for domestic and international reporting purposes, such as net carbon stock fluxes; fluxes on managed forestlands; and changes in carbon stocks from afforestation, reforestation, and deforestation. In general, the data and methods are consistent with U.N. Intergovernmental Panel on Climate Change (IPCC) "Good Practice Guidance" (2003).

This report does, however, contain a number of recommendations that Russian analysts could adopt to reduce the uncertainty related to estimating carbon fluxes from land use change and forest management. For instance, Russian authorities could develop a more systematic forest inventory system that collects additional data, reduces the time between inventories, and provides for additional sampling in regions where remote sensing is used. In addition, because one of the major uncertainties in Russia revolves around carbon emissions from forest fires, Russian authorities could improve estimates of carbon fluxes arising from forest fires by applying remote sensing information on fire area and severity more broadly and combining this information with sampling data from burned areas. These methods would be particularly useful in regions where fire statistics are not currently kept.

2. **What is the magnitude of carbon stocks on lands in Russia today, and are these stocks a net sink or source of emissions?**

Currently, Russia's forestland produces a net carbon sink. There are 289.4 (±71.8) billion tonnes carbon equivalent stored in above- and below-ground pools of forestland. Recent data indicate that annual sequestration (positive changes in stocks) ranges from 40 to 120 million tonnes carbon equivalent per year, depending on the methods used to estimate flux. This study used a deterministic forestry and land use model to project baseline carbon sequestration into the future. This modeled baseline projects that over the next decade, the positive net sequestration rates are likely to remain at current levels, estimated at 70 million tonnes of carbon per year until 2010. Net sequestration, however, is then projected to decline over a 20- to 40-year period. To put these numbers in context, current estimates of energy emissions in

Russia are 411 million tonnes carbon equivalent per year (Secretariat of the UNFCCC, 2004).

3. What is the economic potential to sequester additional carbon on the Russian forest landscape as a climate mitigation option?

It may be possible to sequester up to 20 million tonnes carbon equivalent per year above the current sequestration rate over the next 80 years at a cost of less than $13 per tonne carbon equivalent. For higher costs of $100 per tonne, it appears possible to increase sequestration by 130 million tonnes per year for 100 years.

Given the results of our analysis of these questions, the final section of the report offers a number of recommendations related to data collection and analysis on forest carbon sequestration in the Russian Federation. These recommendations include the following:

- improving the collection of forestry and ecological data to increase the precision of measuring carbon stocks;

- updating inventory data in remote regions, including the collection of additional information and data on forest stocks and forest fires;

- developing a land use and carbon tracking system;

- improving land use modeling capabilities to provide projections of land use, land use change, and forest stocks;

- developing methods to value the opportunity costs of converting agricultural land to forests; and

- continuing to monitor results of existing carbon sequestration demonstration projects and developing additional case studies of carbon offset projects to fully evaluate the potential for implementing large-scale mitigation projects.

This report and the longer technical report on which it is based (Zamolodchikov et al., 2005) result from a unique collaboration between natural and social scientists from collaborating institutions in the Russian Federation and the United States. It is the first such effort to address these issues, and it improves our understanding of the scale and scope of Russian forests'

potential to mitigate the buildup of greenhouse gases (GHGs) in the atmosphere.

1. Introduction, Purpose, and Background

There is widespread concern that the global environment could be affected by anthropogenic emissions of carbon dioxide (CO_2) and other GHGs (McCarthy et al., 2001). In response, experts have suggested that forests could reduce the contribution of energy-related and other emissions to GHG concentrations in the atmosphere via carbon sequestration, which removes CO_2 from the atmosphere via photosynthesis from forest growth and stores it in terrestrial carbon stocks such as trees, soils, and harvested wood products (Metz et al., 2001). The UNFCCC in 1992 formally recognized the potential role that forests can play in helping to reduce the impacts of climate change. Since then, many countries have responded by intensifying their efforts to quantify their current carbon storage in forests, and some countries (including Russia) have engaged in implementation projects aimed at testing the potential for sequestering additional carbon in forests. Activities such as shifting agricultural land back to forests, reducing deforestation, enhancing forest management, or reducing forest fires are management options that could increase the stock of carbon in the world's forests.

A team of Russian and American scientists, nongovernmental organizations, and U.S. government organizations have worked together on an extensive study to assess and employ advanced data and methods to quantify the historic, current, and potential size of the Russian carbon sink. The results of that effort are published in a longer technical report (Zamolodchikov et al., 2005). This report synthesizes and summarizes the findings of the detailed companion technical report for the international climate policy community. Some material and policy analysis included in this synthesis document, however, are not reported in the technical report, which focuses on technical aspects of carbon accounting and sequestration analysis. Both reports are published in Russian and English.

In developing this synthesis report, the authors worked to answer the following questions:

1. What is the status of Russian forestry data for assessing carbon stocks and flows and for conducting analyses of carbon sequestration potential?

2. What is the magnitude of carbon stocks on lands in Russia today, and are these stocks a net sink or source of emissions?

3. What is the economic potential to sequester additional carbon on the Russian forest landscape as a climate mitigation option?

To answer Questions (2) and (3) above, one must first attempt to assess the status of the data sources available in Russia for quantifying carbon stocks and flows. In so doing, this synthesis report summarizes the results of the technical report, assesses the status of data sources for Russia, compares the methods and data to methods used in other countries, and discusses how the data can be used in international processes (Question 1).

The report then uses the data to present estimates of carbon stocks and emissions in current periods (Question 2), to use state-of-the-art economic modeling to project future trends, and to assess climate mitigation potential (Question 3).

1.1 Climate Change, Land Use, and the Russian Land Base

Current scientific consensus estimates imply that it may be possible to sequester 60 to 87 BTCE over the next 50 years in the world's forests (Metz et al., 2001). Although carbon sequestration through land use change and forestry cannot stop potential climate change, this scale of sequestration clearly can be an important complement to climate change policy. Given the potential value that society places on carbon sequestration (estimated to be in the range of $10 to more than $150 per TCE according to Nordhaus and Boyer [2000]), many countries are evaluating their current carbon stocks in forests and considering alternatives for maintaining and increasing these stocks.

The issue of carbon sequestration in forests is vitally important for Russia because of its large forest and agricultural land areas. Forests in Russia cover around 776 million hectares of

land. Russia also contains around 130 million hectares of wetlands, 221 million hectares of agricultural land (see Figure 1-1), and an additional 100 million hectares of land that potentially could be forested (and is officially designated as forestland) but currently are unstocked. Dixon et al. (1994) estimate that Russian forests comprise around 21 percent of the world's total forest stock and potentially 28 percent of the global carbon stock.

It is important for Russia to develop accurate and verifiable estimates of its carbon stocks, because it has a large store of carbon and significant potential to increase this storage to meet UNFCCC requirements and potentially to participate in the Kyoto Protocol (KP). To date, Russia has reported carbon stocks and the change in stocks through current national communications to the UNFCCC (see below). A number of researchers have used Russian data to estimate actual carbon stocks and their changes (see Section 3.2). The data sources for calculating forest biomass inventories, and consequently carbon inventories, in Russia have long been available for Russian scientists to use. However, these data generally have not been available outside of Russia. This lack of information makes the state of Russia's current carbon stock, and potential future carbon stock, less transparent to outside observers.

1.2 International Reporting of Land Use and Carbon Fluxes

Countries that have ratified the UNFCCC must submit annual estimates of GHG emissions from industrial sources, as well as estimates of emissions and sequestration arising from land use change and forestry. National carbon budgets include estimates of carbon stock in forests and other land uses and changes in the budget through land use change, harvesting, management practices, forest fires, and other human activities. The Russian Federation has submitted three national communications to the UNFCCC (available at the UNFCCC Web site: http://unfccc.int/), although annual reports have not been submitted since 2003.

The IPCC has developed a series of methodologies and guidelines for calculating national GHG emissions and removals (IPCC, 2003; Watson et al., 2000). Within Russia, the task for implementing regular inventories of the

Box 1-1:   Units, Conversion Factors, and Acronyms Used in Report

Units	
1 TCE	1 tonne carbon equivalent = 1,000 Kg = 1 Mg (Megagram)
1 MTCE	1 million tonnes carbon equivalent = 1 Tg
1 BTCE	1 billion tonnes carbon equivalent = 1 Gt or Pg
1 TCE	3.67 tonnes CO_2
1 hectare	2.47 acres
US$1	28.5 Rubles
Acronyms	
GHGs	Greenhouse gases (i.e., CO_2, CH_4)
IPCC	Intergovernmental Panel on Climate Change
JI	Joint Implementation
KP	Kyoto Protocol
SFFA	State Forest Fund Account, which includes basic forest inventory data in Russia
UNFCCC	United Nations Framework Convention on Climate Change
COP	Conference of Parties

Figure 1-1.   Land Uses in Russia (adapted from Stolbovoi and McCallum [2002])
Russia has around 776 million hectares of forested land, 128 million hectares of cropland and fallow cropland, and 91 million hectares of pasture land. Most agricultural land is located in the southern and western parts of the country. Forests stretch from the European part of the country to the Far East.

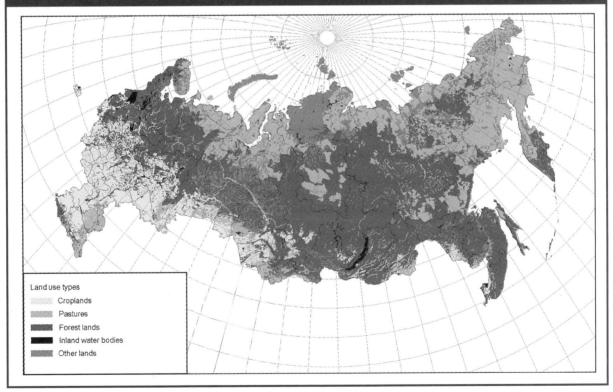

Land use types
- Croplands
- Pastures
- Forest lands
- Inland water bodies
- Other lands

forest stock falls to the Federal Forest Management Agency of the Ministry of Natural Resources. Carbon budgets are calculated by different scientific institutions under the Academy of Sciences, Federal Service for Hydrometeorology and Ministry of Natural Resources.

Russia has now ratified the KP, and the treaty officially came into force in February 2005. The implementation of the KP increases the responsibility of countries that are part of the treaty to report their changes in carbon stocks from land use, land use change, and forestry (LULUCF). In 2001, the 7th Conference of Parties to the UNFCCC (COP7) agreed to a set of rules and guidelines describing how much and which additional human-induced activities in agriculture, land use change, and forestry will be added to and subtracted from the assigned emissions for Annex B Parties to the KP (i.e., countries with emissions reduction commitments under the KP). The agreement establishes principles for identifying, reporting, and reviewing areas of lands subject to LULUCF activities under KP Article 3 for the first commitment period (2008 to 2012).

Several analysts have reviewed the implications of UNFCCC Conference of Parties (COP) decisions on the KP for reporting of LULUCF GHG emissions and activities. Forner (2002) and Kurz et al. (2002), for example, review COP decisions and observe that a Party to the KP may apply decisions on the carbon stock effects of additional human-induced LULUCF activities for the first commitment period (2008 to 2012), provided that these activities have taken place since 1990. Kurz et al. (2002) note that the carbon stock effect attributable to forest management as a result of COP decisions is limited to a) a set of specific narrow practices eligible under KP Article 3.3 (e.g., afforestation, reforestation, and deforestation) and b) additional human-induced activities that must be selected by each Party by 2006 on a voluntary basis under Article 3.4 (e.g., forest management, cropland management, grazing land management, and/or revegetation). The list of selected practices must remain fixed during the first commitment period of the KP. Additionally, each KP Annex B Party has a threshold (cap) on reporting on carbon removals (uptake) from forest management, as well as a limited ability to compensate emissions from

anthropogenic deforestation practices with removals obtained from regular forestry practices (Forner, 2002; Kurz et al., 2002).

A decision by the COP set the forest management reporting caps for Annex B countries for the first commitment period (Forner, 2002). This cap for the Russian Federation is 33 MTCE per year, which includes forest management and afforestation projects under KP Article 6, Joint Implementation (JI). JI project-based activities occur in one Annex B Party's territory, but the emissions reductions or uptake is reported by a second Annex B Party (e.g., by a member of the European Union [EU]) and credited to it by joint, negotiated agreement among the activity's partners (Kurz et al., 2002; Forner, 2002). The reporting on project activities has to be made separately from the reporting on Article 3 activity accounts, which apply to a Party as a whole.

Reporting on forest-based carbon sequestration or emissions in the UNFCCC context concentrates explicitly on net changes from direct human-induced activities on afforestation, reforestation, and deforestation since 1990 that have significant contributions to the overall carbon budget (Kurz et al., 2002). In addition, the reporting must account for emission and removal profiles within national agriculture and forest sectors of the Russian Federation. Specific reporting requirements have been addressed in the IPCC "Good Practice Guidance" for LULUCF, as well as the electronic reporting format elaborated on and agreed to under the UNFCCC in 2004 (IPCC, 2003; and in the following decision undertaken by the COP to the UNFCCC: FCCC/SBSTA/2004/L.26/Add.1).

Russia has already undertaken a number of steps to address these reporting requirements. For instance, a Working Group on Accounting for Greenhouse Gas Emissions and Absorption in Forests within the Framework of the Kyoto Protocol has been established under the Federal Forest Management Agency of the Ministry of Natural Resources of the Russian Federation. Its charge is to assess how the country may best handle the reporting requirements. For the forestry sector in general, the Forestry Code is currently being revised. While this revision is not explicitly related to international reporting requirements, the process is likely to have implications for such reporting as changes are made to land tenure, institutional responsibilities, forest management, and harvesting practices or requirements, for example. It is unclear whether these changes will increase or decrease uncertainty in the estimates of carbon stocks or fluxes from forests of the Russian Federation. Russia also began to develop forestry demonstration projects during the Activities Implemented Jointly (AIJ) Pilot Phase of the UNFCCC in the 1990s to gain experience in the methods and technical issues associated with carbon sequestration projects. However, there is a continued need to supplement the current system of reporting on the national carbon balance with additional information and data. These supplemental needs are discussed in the conclusion to this report.

1.3 Carbon Sequestration as a Climate Change Mitigation Option

In recent years, scientists and policy makers have suggested a number of different options for increasing carbon storage in forests, such as increasing afforestation, reducing deforestation, improving management, undertaking more intensive regeneration efforts, reducing harvests in mature to overmature forests, and reducing the impacts of forest disturbances such as fires. This report examines several of these options, namely afforestation, enhancement of regeneration management in existing forests, reduction of harvests in remote forests, and intensified management to improve forest productivity (i.e., through thinning—harvest of poorly growing trees or overstocked stands).

Two alternative approaches are used in this study for assessing the economic feasibility of these sequestration methods: "bottom-up" and "top-down" approaches. These terms have been widely used within the energy modeling and carbon sequestration literature to broadly represent two different ways of estimating unit costs of sequestration. Bottom-up methods use detailed data on costs and carbon sequestration potential from activity data or individual projects to estimate the GHG benefits and economic costs of engaging in those practices. These methods usually result in *average* cost estimates (the cost of the practice divided by all of the carbon sequestered), rather than *marginal* cost estimates (the cost of the last unit of carbon sequestered), although they can be used to generate marginal cost functions in some cases.

Top-down methods, in contrast, use fairly aggregated (often national-scale) data within economic models to estimate the marginal costs of varying levels of carbon sequestration. Marginal cost analysis is helpful for identifying the efficient mix of options at various levels of sequestration. An efficient mix occurs when the marginal costs of all sequestration options are the same. In other words, with the efficient mix it is not possible to reduce overall costs of achieving a given sequestration level by switching from one option to another.

In addition to considering potential future sequestration opportunities, this report reviews several current carbon sequestration projects underway in Russia. These projects, RUSAFOR-SAP in Saratov Oblast and a shelter belt program in Voronezh Oblast, provide supporting evidence of sequestration options that can be implemented in Russia.

2. Available Data for Reporting Russian Carbon Stocks and Fluxes

This section summarizes the data and methods used to estimate land uses, carbon stocks, and carbon fluxes. Most primary data sources are in the Russian language, and more detailed information on these sources can be found in the technical report (Zamolodchikov et al., 2005). The end of this section describes the relevance of these data sources for reporting carbon stock changes and mitigation activities.

2.1 Steps Necessary for Quantifying Carbon in Forests

Quantifying the amount of carbon in a terrestrial ecosystem is complicated by the fact that aggregate carbon stocks are generally not observed or measured directly for entire pools, landscapes, regions, or countries. If they were, one could simply sum the measurements and report this total as the carbon stock for the area in question. However, the estimates of aggregate carbon stocks can be made only indirectly, using directly obtained data on ecosystem conditions and associated models or data on changes in carbon stocks by ecosystem component (see Figure 2-1).

Figure 2-1. Quantifying National Terrestrial Carbon Stocks over Time
Carbon stocks are not directly measured at the regional or national level but estimated through the application of carbon parameters to natural resource data for the area in question. Both natural resource conditions and carbon dynamics can change over time, thereby affecting carbon projections.

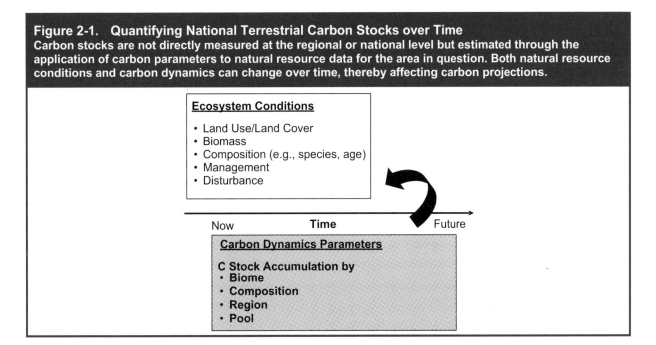

Data on ecosystem conditions such as land use/land cover, vegetation type, volume of growing stock, management regimes, and disturbance are typically part of natural resource inventory data. Inventory data may be either remotely sensed or measured on the ground (i.e., ground based). Data are generally available in most regions, although at different levels of resolution and precision.

The data used to characterize ecosystem components must be combined with information on the carbon content of each component to develop estimates of carbon budget. These parameters can, in principle, be derived from complex ecosystem process models or can be developed from standard growth and yield tables by ecosystem type and condition (e.g., carbon storage per hectare by region, tree species, age class, stand density, and management regime).

Within Russia, as in other countries, it is necessary to carefully distinguish between biophysical and administrative definitions and classifications of forests. These are easily confused, because different types of land use often go under the same name (such as "forest"). A forest in a biophysical sense may grow either on land that is legally designated as forestland (and thus the administrative and reporting responsibility of one particular government agency) or on land designated as agricultural land (and the responsibility of another agency).

The legal designation is purely administrative and need not necessarily reflect the actual land cover. This fact is important to consider when assessing the permanence of potential sequestration options (e.g., how long the effect of mitigation activities like afforestation will persist before becoming reversed because of market, other economic, or institutional factors). For instance, forest established on land legally designated as agricultural land in Russia may be more likely to be converted back to agricultural use than forest established on land designated as forestland. Information on the legal designation of the land is described in this report, although we assume that activities that sequester carbon can occur on all types of legally designated land (e.g., agricultural lands legally defined as agricultural are allowed to convert to forests in some of the sequestration scenarios described in Section 5 below).

2.2 Data for Estimating Land Use

As noted in the introduction, the technical report that accompanies this document contains detailed information on data sources and the use of that data for estimating land use, land use change, and carbon fluxes (see Zamolodchikov et al., 2005). Readers interested in more detail on the specific methodologies used to construct the datasets used in this analysis are referred to that report.

Data in this report are derived from the State Forest Fund Account (SFFA), the State Land Account (SLA), and other statistical reports on forest and agricultural management. These data are gathered and published by several governmental departments in the Russian Federation that have management authority over the land. Figure 2-2 shows the structure of governmental departments regulating forests and forestry in Russia circa mid-2005. It should be noted that this structure has been subjected to substantial changes in recent years.

The two main agencies responsible for controlling forestland in Russia are the Ministry of Natural Resources and the Ministry of

Agriculture. Current estimates suggest that there are 1,179 million hectares of forestland in Russia, with 96.0 percent of the hectares under the jurisdiction of the Ministry of Natural Resources. The Ministry of Natural Resources controls the SFFA through a subagency, the Federal Forest Management Agency (formerly the Federal Forest Service). Only 3.4 percent of Russia's forestland area is currently controlled by the Ministry of Agriculture, and less than 1 percent of forestland in Russia is under the control of the Ministry of Education, Ministry of Defense, and various city authorities (Forest Account, 2004). Trees growing on some types of private land in Russia (e.g., villages, country houses, homestead lands) are not included in

Figure 2-2. Russian Federation Ministries and Departments Collecting and Publishing Data on Forestry

This diagram shows links and information flows across ministries and departments within the Russian Federation that collect and manage official data on the state forest accounts, agricultural accounts, and statistical reports on forestry and agriculture. The Ministry of Natural Resources and the Ministry of Agriculture have undergone several reorganizations in recent years, and the governance structure may not yet have stabilized. The figure shows the situation circa mid-2005.

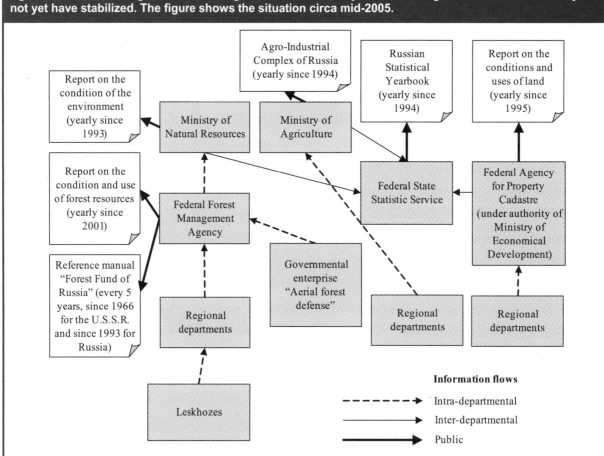

the SFFA and so are not considered in this study. Detailed information on tree species and age group distributions are published only for forests under jurisdiction of the Ministry of Natural Resources. The calculations in this document use Ministry of Natural Resources data (96 percent of forestland area) to estimate the forest age class distribution and carbon characteristics. This information is extrapolated to estimate carbon storage on the remaining 4 percent of forestland area.

2.2.1 Forestland and Growing Stock Inventories in the State Forest Fund Account

Forests within the SFFA are divided into local management units, each of which is called a *leskhoz*. The SFFA is a compilation of forest inventory information that is reported to the Federal Forest Management Agency. Before 2000, this information was reported every 5 years. Since 2000, this information has been reported annually. Detailed information is available annually within the federal government. A detailed report is disseminated publicly every 5 years by the Federal Forest Management Agency. Information on final felling, thinning, fires, reforestation, and related activities is reported by *leskhozes* annually, and general summaries are published in annual reports of the Ministry of Natural Resources.

The general methods of forest inventory collection used in the Russian Federation are shown in Figure 2-3 and are summarized in Box 2-1. Three types of inventories are used within Russia. For forests in economically important *leskhozes* (i.e., those with active logging and forest management), ground inventories are conducted every 5 to 10 years. This inventory involves a preliminary delineation of stands by photo-interpretation and subsequent verification and measurements of each stand in the field. Information is collected on dominant species type, age class, growing stock volume, regeneration intensity, and many other characteristics of the site and stand. Each *leskhoz* will update information on forestland areas, forest types, stocking conditions, and other information as they change because of logging, fires, windthrow, insect infestations, and growth.

This periodic ground-based inventory system applies to 731 million hectares (62 percent of the SFFA). Approximately 47 percent of the land within this area has been inventoried within the last 10 years. Current estimates suggest that sampling errors at the national level for lands inventoried in this way are approximately +/– 2 to 5 percent.

For the remaining 53 percent of the area subject to ground-based inventory, the interval between inventories has increased to more than 10 years. This is longer than the standard that has been set in some other countries, such as the United States and Sweden (Table 2-1), where sample plots are inventoried every 5 years. Canada, however, has developed a new system of plots that have all been measured since 2001 but will be sampled every 10 years in the future (Gillis, 2001). To improve the quality of data collection in forests that are regularly sampled with ground-based inventory methods, Russia should consider developing a network system of plots representative of these forest types, which should be remeasured at least once every 10 years.

The remaining 448 million hectares (or 38 percent) of lands in the SFFA are not currently subject to ground-based inventories; however, 370 million hectares (31 percent) of forests in SFFA have been inventoried with remote sensing, including photo-interpretation and satellite imagery methods (Box 2-1). Similar technologies are used widely in remote areas of Canada and in the United States. In Canada, remotely sensed data are combined with sample data from established inventory plots and used in a carbon budgeting model to estimate carbon stocks and fluxes (Kurz and Apps, 2005). Russia has a similar system when using remote sensing, although less intensive ground-based sampling and modeling are currently being applied. In the future, Russia should consider enhancing the estimates of carbon stocks and fluxes in remote regions by combining remote sensing, ground-based sampling, and modeling tools. The final 78 million hectares (7 percent) of SFFA land was last inventoried in the 1950s through aero-visual techniques, which involve observations of forestland taken by individuals in airplanes flying over the forests. Continued efforts to improve the use of remote sensing techniques will enable Russia to update data in areas using these aero-visual techniques.

Figure 2-3.   Flow Chart Illustrating Forestry Data Collection, Processing, and Reporting for the State Forest Fund Account in the Russian Federation
This simplified chart illustrates basic steps and procedures applied nationally for collecting forestry data within the territory of the Russian Federation. These procedures are implemented in accordance with unified national guidelines with modification by geographical region and dominant tree species. The entire results of forestland and state forest stock inventories are regularly published in the reference books (State Forest Fund Account).

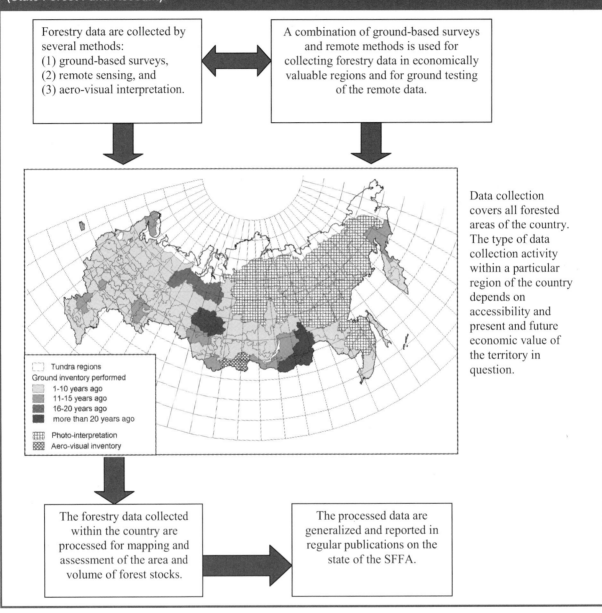

Forestry data are collected by several methods:
(1) ground-based surveys,
(2) remote sensing, and
(3) aero-visual interpretation.

A combination of ground-based surveys and remote methods is used for collecting forestry data in economically valuable regions and for ground testing of the remote data.

Data collection covers all forested areas of the country. The type of data collection activity within a particular region of the country depends on accessibility and present and future economic value of the territory in question.

Tundra regions
Ground inventory performed
1-10 years ago
11-15 years ago
16-20 years ago
more than 20 years ago

Photo-interpretation
Aero-visual inventory

The forestry data collected within the country are processed for mapping and assessment of the area and volume of forest stocks.

The processed data are generalized and reported in regular publications on the state of the SFFA.

Box 2-1:   How Are Forest Inventories Conducted in Russia?

The SFFA is a compilation of summary data from different inventories conducted locally and reported to the federal government every 5 years by the local state forest management units (*leskhozes*). Annual reporting began in 2004. There are approximately 1,179 million hectares in the SFFA in 2003. Lands are inventoried in one of three ways:

- *Periodic Ground-Inventoried Forests* (62 percent of the area; 731 million hectares): These forests are subject to recurrent stand-level ground inventory according to standard international practice. Approximately 47 percent of ground-inventoried forests, or 344 million hectares, were sampled in the past 10 years.

- *Periodic Remotely Sensed Forests* (31 percent of the area; 370 million hectares): Inventories are conducted via photo-interpretation of aerial photographs and satellite images approximately every 20 to 25 years without field verification.

- *Aero-Visual Inventoried Forests* (7 percent; 78 million hectares): Inventories were last conducted in the 1950s by visual observations, which involved individual observers taking notes on a map while flying over the forest.

The geographical distribution of these three methods of forest inventories is shown in Figure 2-3.

Despite the relatively low estimates of aggregate error in the ground-based inventories, there is some evidence that the estimation of growing stock volume in Russian forests is systematically biased downward (i.e., it may underestimate true growing stock volume). Current estimates suggest that this bias could lead to underreporting growing stock by up to 30 percent (Alexeyev and Birdsey, 1994 [in Russian] or 1998 [in English]; Filipchuk et al., 2000). These biases appear to occur most frequently when estimating growing stock on young stands and on old, multistory stands. Although a number of studies have been conducted to assess the validity of the potential for systematically underestimating inventories, for the purposes of this study, no such adjustments to inventories have been made. This is a significant source of uncertainty in these estimates.

The methods used for data collection and estimation in Russia are generally consistent with the IPCC "Good Practice Guidance" (IPCC, 2003), as well as techniques used in different countries. Ground-based inventories are used on 731 million hectares of forestland in Russia. Around 53 percent of the ground-based inventory data are more than 10 years old. As noted above, these data are older than the standard that has been set in some other countries, such as the United States and Sweden (Table 2-1). The IPCC "Good Practice Guidance"

offers ideas for forests that are regularly sampled. To be consistent with these recommendations, Russia should consider developing a system of gridded plots for forests that are regularly sampled with ground-based inventories and consider establishing program goals of remeasuring these plots at least once very 10 years.

Another 370 million hectares of forestland in Russia are inventoried with remote sensing technologies. Similar technologies are used widely in remote areas of Canada and in the United States, although Russia employs less intensive use of ground-based sampling and modeling. Russia could enhance estimates of carbon stocks and fluxes in remote regions through more intensive sampling and remote sensing in the future.

No other countries in Table 2-1 currently use the aero-visual techniques that are used on 78 million hectares of Russian forestlands. Russia should continue developing remote sensing and ground-based sampling methodologies to update these data in particular.

2.2.2 Forest Disturbances

The evolution of forest carbon stocks over time is heavily dependent on the frequency and extent of disturbances from natural sources, such as fire, and human sources, such as timber harvesting. Data for each of these phenomena are described below.

Table 2-1: **Comparison of Russian Federation and Other Boreal Country Land Cover, Land Use, and Carbon Budget Data and Methods**

Country	Forest Area: Inventory	Forest Area: Remote Sensing	Carbon Budget: Inventory	Frequency of Data Collection of Forest Area	Publishing Frequency
Canada[a]	Whole area using aerial photography, remote sensing, and ground plots.	Used throughout Canada but more heavily in northern regions.	Under development, based on ground plots.	5 to 10 years for National Forest Inventory. Annual for disturbances (fire, insects).	Fire: Annual; Forest Inventory: every 5 years; carbon: likely annual.
Russian Federation	Whole area inventory using either ground-based inventories, remote sensing, or aero-visual inventory.	Actively used in inventory of least accessible forests.	Absent presently. Noninventory estimates available.	10 years for ground-based inventories. 5 to 40 years for photo-interpretation inventories. Aero-visual inventories phased out. Annual for disturbances (fires, clear cuts, insects) and reforestation in productive areas.	Every 5 years for areas and stocks. Annually for disturbances and reforestation.
Sweden	Whole area, all land categories, through sample plots (some permanent). No aggregation of data for treatment units.	Annual coverage for whole country at 10 to 20 m resolution; used to generalize sample plot measurements.	No dedicated system; national forest survey data are used.	Whole country sampled annually. Intensity is greater in regions with higher productivity.	Annually for logging, fires, etc. Growing stock and increment every 5 years at country level, every 10 years at district level.
United States[b]	Plot inventory, 5 to 15 years, moving to annual.	Used in sampling design to help calculate forest area.	Annual estimates for private lands; periodic estimates for public lands.	1 year some areas. 5 years other areas. 10 to 15 remote areas.	Data available on Internet. Summary reports provided annually for private lands and public lands, except Alaska and Hawaii.

[a]Werner Kurz of Natural Resources Canada provided information on inventory methods in Canada.

[b]Richard Birdsey of the U.S. Forest Service provided information on inventory methods in the United States.

Forest Fires

Forest fires are directly observed and managed with land-based fire fighting or aerial protection on 67 percent of SFFA and other forested areas. For each fire that is observed and for those fires that are extinguished, data on the area burned is recorded by the fire protection agency. Aggregated data on the area of fires that occur, as well as the type of fire (crown fire versus ground fire) are maintained by the Russian Federation State Committee on Statistics (*Goskomstat*). The character and volume of information on forest fires in the Russian Federation allows a first-order estimation of the size of yearly carbon emissions due to forest fires only for the fire-protected area of the SFFA. On the remaining 33 percent of forestland, fires are neither detected nor fought. These areas are generally remote and not subject to forest management. The size of carbon emissions from fires on the unprotected territories for this report has been estimated by using fire rates on protected areas and models of stand dynamics during and after fires and applying those to areas that are not protected. In principal, however, it is possible to use more intensive remote sensing methods combined with sample data to estimate emissions in regions where there is no fire protection.

Timber Harvesting

Data on harvests are obtained through public reports from the Federal Forest Management Agency and Ministry of Natural Resources. Within Russia, 331.5 million hectares (33 percent of the total SFFA area) are designated for industrial use. The remaining area of land is currently set aside from harvesting. Currently, the allowable annual cut for Russia is 500 million m³ per year, 300 million m³ of which is in allowable annual cut, and in recent years, substantially lower. In the 1990s, only about 25 percent of the annual allowable cut was harvested in any year. There is some concern that unrecorded forest harvesting occurs in Russia (i.e., harvests that occur in violation of forest legislation). According to data from the Ministry of Natural Resources, illegal harvests are less than 1 percent of total annual harvest (ARISMF, 2003). Illegal harvests, therefore, appear to have minor effects on overall carbon fluxes, and we have not included estimates of these potential additional harvest flows in this analysis.

2.2.3 Wetlands and Agricultural Land Area

Wetlands and agricultural land constitute two other large land uses in the Russian Federation that can have important implications for *forest* carbon sequestration. Many wetlands are located on land managed by the Federal Forest Management Agency. Agricultural land constitutes a large area of potential land for carbon sequestration projects through afforestation.

Wetlands

Estimates of the total area of wetlands in Russia vary widely across the methods different authors have used to estimate wetland area (see Section 3 below). The SFFA inventory compilations for 1998 and 2003 indicated that

there were *approximately 131 million hectares of wetlands*, the value used in this report. The SLA includes more land categories than the SFFA and provides a slightly higher estimate of 140 million hectares of wetlands.

Agricultural Land

The information on the area of agricultural lands and types of their development can be obtained from the SLA maintained by the Federal Agency for Property Cadastre and annual reports from the Ministry of Agriculture. Agricultural lands in this report are accounted only for lands controlled by the Ministry of Agriculture. Inventories for the SLA are conducted annually. The Ministry of Agriculture also controls and maintains inventories on about 3.4 percent of total forestland in Russia. One concern with data in the SLA is that the same land types can be classified into several different uses (e.g., wetlands can be classified in the SFFA, water fund, agricultural lands, or protected areas). Recently passed legislation on the land code in the Russian Federation coupled with KP ratification significantly strengthens the requirements for quality in the SLA.

2.3 Cross-Validation of Forest Area Estimates (SFFA) and Satellite Data

To evaluate their accuracy, SFFA data (Forest Account, 2003) were compared to independent data from the Northern Eurasia Ecosystem Map (NEEM) (Figure 2-4). NEEM was developed as part of the Global Land Cover 2000 project (Bartalev, Belvard, and Ershov, 2002; Bartalev et al., 2003). That map is based on 1-kilometer resolution data from the VEGETATION system on board the French Satellite, SPOT. The SPOT-VEGETATION system continually observes the condition of vegetation cover around the globe.

A comparison of the area covered by forest for Russia as a whole, according to the two separate data sources, shows very high correlation between the SFFA and NEEM. The aggregate difference is only about 0.3 percent. This high correlation demonstrates that field inventory SFFA state forestland area estimates are reliable and very close to satellite remote sensing estimates of forest area. The results also indicate a high level of positive correlation

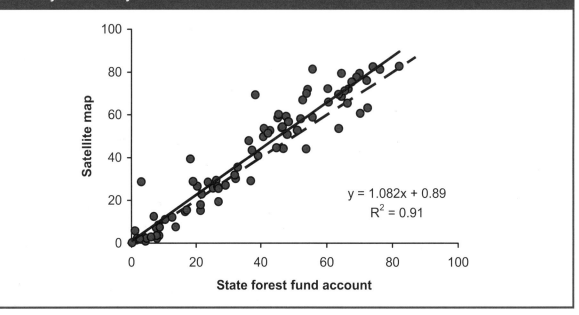

Figure 2-4.   Percentage of Forestland in the SFFA Inventory and in the Satellite-Based Northern Eurasia Ecosystem Map (NEEM)
The figure compares SFFA inventory data (Forest Account, 2003) for Oblasts and Krai with estimates made using satellite imagery. The 45-degree line indicates perfect correlation between the two datasets. The hatched line is slightly less than 45 degrees, suggesting a less than perfect, but close, correlation between field inventory and remotely sensed land area estimates.

between the area predictions in each region of Russia. The areas with the least precise correlation occur mainly in the European part of Russia, where a larger proportion of forests are maintained by the Ministry of Agriculture or agencies besides the Ministry of Natural Resources (Figure 2-4).

2.4   Estimating Carbon Stocks and Fluxes

Once the area of land under various cover types is determined, total carbon storage can be estimated by combining the land area data with models or data that quantify the carbon density and sequestration rates of the various land covers. The technical report (Zamolodchikov et al., 2005) includes substantial detail on methods that can be used to estimate carbon in forest, wetland, and agricultural ecosystems. Those methods are discussed briefly.

2.4.1 Carbon in Forested Ecosystems
A number of studies have been conducted in Russia to relate the growing stock volume of forests to carbon storage (i.e., Isaev et al., 1993, 1995; Utkin et al., 2001; Utkin et al., 2002; and

Utkin, 2003). Phytomass (live biomass) in the lower layer vegetation of a given forest stand can be estimated by calculating average phytomass for each forest type (determined by predominant species and geographical subzones) using the database from Utkin et al. (1994). Estimates of carbon in soil are based on data from the SFFA and the average soil carbon content per hectare (Chestnykh et al., 1999; Chestnykh, Zamolodchikov, and Utkin, 2004).

The effects of logging on carbon stocks and fluxes can be estimated using information on

- the volume of harvested and extracted wood disaggregated by forest-species group;

- reports on the condition of felling sites, which include information on volumes of abandoned merchantable timber and the extent of thinning, for example; and

- information on the volume of harvest residuals (stumps, roots, branches, treetops).

Residual volumes are estimated using conversion coefficients for mature and overmature forests of the applicable species groups.

Carbon emissions from forest fires can be estimated using data on the area and composition of burned areas and also on the amount of forest fuel materials burned in crown, ground, and soil fires (Isaev et al., 1995). The size of post-fire tree mortality is calculated using data on the area of forests that die due to fires and the average volume of carbon in those forests, calculated as described above.

2.4.2 Carbon in Wetlands and Agricultural Lands

Wetlands

The estimate of the carbon pool in wetlands in this study is based on wetland area estimates from the SFFA, where wetlands are a category of nonforestland. Estimates for the average carbon stored in plant biomass per hectare are derived by combining published results from several studies, as reported in Zamolodchikov et al. (2005). Average soil carbon content per hectare is derived from Chestnykh et al. (1999, 2004). Neither disturbances nor methane emissions are included in the estimates reported here.

Agricultural Land

Carbon in agricultural soils is estimated using data on agro-chemical characteristics and regional distributions of the main soil types (Kononova, 1984; Dyakonova et al., 1984; Orlov, Biryukova, and Sukhanova, 1996; Tyurin, 1937). Carbon stocks are calculated for each main category of agricultural land (crop land, grazing land, other land), as well as crop types.

2.5 Summary Assessment of Data Availability and Quality for National Reporting of Carbon Fluxes and Mitigation Activities

The results of the Zamolodchikov et al. (2005) technical report suggest that the data are generally available for Russia to report annual carbon emissions and sequestration in forests. For example (Tables 2-2 and 2-3), under the UNFCCC Convention Article 4.1 and Article 12, countries need to report emissions and uptake on forest and agricultural lands and carbon pools on them. For Convention Article 4.1(b), countries are to report land area in national or regional mitigation programs and, in Article 4.1(d), land area and GHG benefits from

promoting conservation and enhancement of sinks. The technical report by Zamolodchikov et al. (2005) provides detailed discussion of the potential sources of such data.

Reporting of mitigation activities requires data on land use, area, and GHG fluxes, available over different spatial and temporal resolutions. Detailed international discussion and guidance development have occurred on the methods for reporting mitigation activities. For example, Kurz et al. (2002) note that countries like Russia contemplating reporting internationally on future mitigation activities in the LULUCF sector would need to account for land use change arising from reforestation, afforestation, avoided deforestation, or other activities that have occurred since a given base-year starting date. Mitigation reporting also would need to reflect only those activities and carbon fluxes occurring within a temporal window specified by a given program. The land use/land cover data described in Zamolodchikov et al. (2005) and summarized in this report indicate that Russia is likely to be able to meet these requirements and could do so within the confines of the IPCC "Good Practice Guidance" (IPCC, 2003), which offer detailed guidance on such reporting. Relevant data for reporting forestry mitigation activities include the SFFA data, data from the Ministry of Agriculture, and the remote sensing analysis described in Section 2.3.

Russia also appears to have the data necessary to identify lands under forest management as a land use category for the purposes of reporting mitigation activities. Some authors (e.g., Kurz et al. [2002]) have noted that countries may review their currently proposed mitigation activity categories in the LULUCF sector and elect to include additional forestry activities such as forest management in their national GHG inventories and mitigation reports. As noted above, ground-based inventory information on forest areas and growing stock volume by dominant tree species and age classes is available on 62 percent of Russian forestland. Only 42 percent of this land has been inventoried in the past 10 years. However, if additional data and methods development efforts are undertaken in Russia over the next 5 or so years, Russia may well be in a position to have adequate data to be able to identify additional forest mitigation activities on

Table 2-2: International LULUCF Reporting to UNFCCC and Russian Data Availability

Reporting Topic	Purpose of Reporting	Data Availability and Potential Enhancements
Reporting GHG Emissions and Uptake Report on national GHG emissions and removals by sinks (annual or semiannual): • emissions and uptake on forest and agricultural lands • pools included in the reporting	Convention, Article 4.1 (a) and Article 12	Data available (SFFA, studies on forest biomass and the data of Ministry of Agriculture, Federal Agency for Property Cadastre and Federal State Statistic Agency) to estimate emissions and sinks. • Potential to reduce time between ground inventories and eliminate use of aero-visual techniques. • Potential to update and improve inventory and ecological data collected on national forest stock in all regions. • Could update forest fire flux calculations, particularly in remote regions.
Reporting Land Management for Forest Conservation and Mitigation of GHGs Land area in national or regional mitigation programs	Convention, Article 4.1 (b)	Data likely available. • Probably no improvements necessary.
Land area and GHG benefits from promoting conservation and enhancement of sinks.	Convention, Article 4.1 (d)	Data likely available. • May need to assess if data available and methods adequate.

Notes: Convention means UNFCCC Convention; GHGs means greenhouse gases.

Source: UNFCCC Convention

Table 2-3: Representative Topics in LULUCF Mitigation Reporting and Russian Data Availability

Reporting Topic	Data Availability and Potential Enhancements
Area of land defined as given land type (e.g., "forest")	Data available from SFFA. • Likely need to define and report area of forest in base year. • Option to develop a system to identify and track area changes from base year and over time.
Area by management class (e.g., managed forest, unmanaged forest, inaccessible)	Data available from SFFA. • Could develop criteria for defining "managed" vs. "unmanaged" or other forest categories and subdivide national forest land by managed and unmanaged forests. • Option to track changes in managed forests including forest area, harvests, deforestation, afforestation, etc. from base year over time.
Area from a given base year reforested or afforested (nonforest in base year to forest), and carbon stock change in a future reporting period	Available (SFFA and Ministry of Agriculture, Federal Agency for Property Cadastre and Federal State Statistic Agency). • Could compare ground data to data collection from satellite imagery. • Could revise estimates of land use in forests on agricultural areas. • May need to track land in agriculture from the base year.
Area deforested (forest to nonforest) from a base year, and carbon stock change in reporting period	Available (SFFA and Ministry of Agriculture). • May need to explain how to differentiate between deforestation (change of land use) and forest harvesting with regard to national context.
Area under broad land management categories (like forest, agricultural, or grazing land management, or revegetation not yet resulting in forest)	Forest data available (SFFA). Crop and grazing land data available from Ministry of Agriculture. • Assess if data are available and methods adequate. • Revegetation data possibly available from inventory and remote sensing data from SFFA and other ministries.
Area under carbon sequestration projects	Data available to determine previous land use. Land activity reports available from various agencies. • Assess if data available and methods adequate. • May need to continue monitoring.

actively managed forestlands. As noted in Section 2.2.1, these efforts could include developing more systematic measurement across a network system of plots that are remeasured every 10 years.

An additional 31 percent of forestland area is inventoried with photo-interpretation and therefore is not as specific with respect to age classes. On these lands, if additional sampling on ground inventory plots were undertaken, Russia potentially could reduce the uncertainty inherent in estimating carbon fluxes with remote sensing methodologies. The remaining 7 percent of forestland was last surveyed in the 1950s and would need to be updated with ground-based inventories or remote sensing to reduce the current large uncertainties in carbon flux estimates on these lands.

The results in the technical report (Zamolodchikov et al., 2005) support the general conclusion that Russia appears to have sufficient data to account for land use change and carbon fluxes on lands actively managed under potential forest mitigation options of afforestation, reforestation, or avoided deforestation. It also could potentially account for lands managed under a broad array of forest or agricultural land management practices and carbon fluxes on them; and for carbon sequestration projects occurring at smaller scales as well. Russian data limitations on lands less actively managed (and generally more inaccessible) are significant, however, and careful data quality and methodological assessment would be warranted before any consideration of reporting mitigation activities on these lands.

Despite this general conclusion, several limitations are apparent in the data and merit additional research. Kurz et al. (2002) report that Canada, and hence other large forested countries like Russia, could improve monitoring of mitigation activities by establishing a land and carbon stock tracking system to identify and track lands in forest and agricultural use at a given date and thereafter. They suggest that any such land-tracking system may need to include harvested areas (so they are not reported as deforestation), and natural disturbance and forest management areas as well (e.g., Kurz et al., 2002). Agricultural land areas can be calculated currently with data from the Ministry of Agriculture, but as noted above, there are

small discrepancies between satellite imagery and the SFFA data for forestland cover. Deforestation is not presently considered a substantial threat within Russia. Data on deforestation, however, would be available through the inventory procedures developed for the SFFA.

Improvements in sampling where remotely sensed data are used may assist Russia in its reporting, as discussed above. In addition, one major consideration for Russia revolves around accounting for fluxes from important disturbances, like forest fires. Fire area and damage in regions where forest fire protection is not provided are not presently calculated. It is possible to use a combination of remote sensing (to detect areas where fires occur) and sampling data from actual fires to estimate carbon fluxes associated with all fires in Russia (as done in other countries, such as Canada).

Several prototype carbon sequestration demonstration projects, as described below, have already begun in Russia. Monitoring reports on these projects may help Russian analysts design and report on future project-level mitigation and identify promising, cost-effective activities and locations for potential project investment. Carbon fluxes on these lands potentially could be tracked using a tracking system discussed by Kurz et al. (2002) to illustrate that such project activities are additional to business-as-usual activities (if required in a mitigation program) and are not double counted in national-scale land accounting.

One institutional aspect of potential reporting of LULUCF data is that the administrative boundaries between agencies and their land management responsibilities continue to evolve in Russia. This may have implications for forest and other land data collection and reporting over time. The data for this report are current as of August 2004. Future changes in the administrative responsibilities of different agencies could shift the names of the agencies responsible for reporting data for the UNFCCC processes.

3. Historical Trends in Land Use, Carbon Stocks, and Fluxes for Russia (1966 to 2003)

This section explores the second major question addressed by this report, namely, what is the current estimate of carbon stocks and fluxes in Russia? The methods, data, and parameters for the results presented in this section are available in the accompanying technical report (Zamolodchikov et al., 2005).

3.1 Trends in Land Cover, Disturbances, and Carbon Sequestration

Several important trends are examined in this section, including trends in forest area and stocking; disturbance patterns, including fires and harvesting; and wetland areas and agricultural lands.

3.1.1 Forest Area and Carbon Stocks

Forestland Area Trends

Forestland area maintained by the SFFA has increased from around 706 to 776 million hectares since the 1960s (Table 3-1). Growing stock has increased from 77 to 82 billion m³. Although total forestland has increased, the proportion of coniferous forests has declined from 74 percent in 1966 to around 70 percent presently, and the area of shrub land and nonregenerated forestland has increased from around 7 percent in 1966 to 10 percent today. The area of overmature forests has declined from 63 percent of forestland area in 1966 to 48 percent today because of timber extraction from the 1960s to early 1990s.

The "nonforested area" category in Table 3-1 includes sparse stands, burned out and dead stands, logged over stands, and clearings and gaps. Sparse stands and burned out stands make up the bulk of land in this category, accounting for 70 and 27 million hectares, respectively, in 2003 (40 to 60 percent of these stands are located in or near the tundra). The official statistics report a two- to threefold drop in area of cutover stands during the period, which is attributed to a decrease in the volume of logging, as well as a shift from clear cutting to selective logging. The category "other land area" in Table 3-1 includes areas that cannot be forested because of low productivity or because they are wetlands. Wetlands account for around 45 percent of the area in this category, or an estimated 130 million hectares in 2003.

Forest Carbon Stock Trends

Total carbon stocks in living tree biomass in Russia have been relatively stable at around 34 BTCE since 1966 (Table 3-2). Most of the carbon stock is locked up in coniferous forests, although the proportion in conifer forests has declined since 1966 mainly because of more intensive harvesting activity. Hardwood and deciduous softwood carbon stocks, in contrast, have increased since 1966.

Using the estimated change in the age class distribution of forests, average annual accumulation of carbon in living tree biomass is estimated as 239 MTCE per year between 1993 and 2003. More than 65 percent of this accumulation occurs in young stands. These estimated gains are gross calculations based on annual growth in forests, and they will be offset, at least to some extent, by emissions from harvests, fires, and other disturbances (discussed below). One way to account for the net effects of all these factors is to assess net stock differences between successive inventories. Based on this information, net annual carbon growth is estimated to be around 40 MTCE per year for the period 1993 to 2003.

The store of organic carbon in the soil (0 to 100 cm deep) is significantly larger than the carbon stored in above-ground vegetation, as is common in temperate and boreal ecosystems. Estimates of the soil carbon stock in Russia based on the existing data and SFFA forest areas range from 112 to 126 BTCE over the period 1966 to 2003. Soil carbon stocks tend to be a function of forest area and therefore do not change substantially from year to year.

3.1.2 Harvesting, Regeneration, and Disturbance

The accumulation of forest carbon stocks depends critically on the level of harvest and regeneration activity and other disturbances on the landscape. Trends in these activities and their carbon consequences are described below.

Table 3-1:   **Area of Russian Forest Fund Lands, 1996 to 2003, Derived from the State Forest Fund Account**

	1966	1973	1978	1983	1988	1993	1998	2003
	Million Hectares							
Forested area	705.6	729.7	766.3	771.1	763.5	763.5	774.2	776.1
Nonforested area	157.4	132.4	113.9	113.0	123.0	123.0	107.8	106.8
Other land area	298.9	299.3	313.9	298.5	294.4	294.4	296.6	296.0
Total SFFA land area	1,161.9	1,161.4	1,194.1	1,182.6	1,180.9	1,180.9	1,178.6	1,178.9
	Billion m^3							
Growing stock volume	77	79.7	81.7	81.9	81.7	80.7	81.9	82.1

Table 3-2:   **Forest Carbon Stocks in Living Biomass, 1966 to 2003, Based on Forested Area Estimates from State Forest Fund Account**

	BTCE							
	1966	1973	1978	1983	1988	1993	1998	2003
Coniferous	26.7	27.0	27.3	27.5	27.1	25.8	25.7	25.5
Deciduous hardwood	1.1	1.2	1.1	1.2	1.1	1.2	1.2	1.2
Deciduous softwood	5.3	5.1	5.2	5.2	5.1	5.3	5.6	5.9
Shrub/other	1.3	1.3	1.3	1.3	1.4	1.5	1.5	1.5
Total	34.4	34.6	34.9	35.2	34.7	33.8	34.0	34.1

Harvesting Activity and Emissions

Harvesting Trends. Since the early 1990s, timber harvests in Russia fell by over 50 percent (Figure 3-1). These reductions occurred as economic growth declined, traditional ties to trading partners in Eastern Europe were opened to additional competition from European suppliers, and disinvestment occurred in the large industrial structure that supported the timber industry. More recently, these trends have begun to reverse, and there is renewed growth in annual harvests in Russia. *From their low of 129 million m³ in annual production in 1998, timber harvests rose 23 percent to 153 million m³ per year by 2002.* There is speculation that illegal timber harvests in Russia's Far East could induce additional harvesting beyond the official statistics, but as noted above, these numbers are not considered in this report.

Carbon Emissions from Harvesting. From 1990 to 1992, emissions from harvesting are estimated to range from 96 to 119 MTCE per year. From 1993 to 1998, harvest emissions fell to around 47 MTCE per year, bringing the average figure for the 1990s to 69 MTCE per year. Of that amount, 39 MTCE per year come from harvested stem wood and 30 MTCE per year from decaying deadwood, some of which includes merchantable timber left at the cutting site. Official data may understate this latter number, which may introduce additional uncertainty into carbon estimates. Note that the historical estimates of harvest emissions presented in this section do not account for carbon stored in wood products.

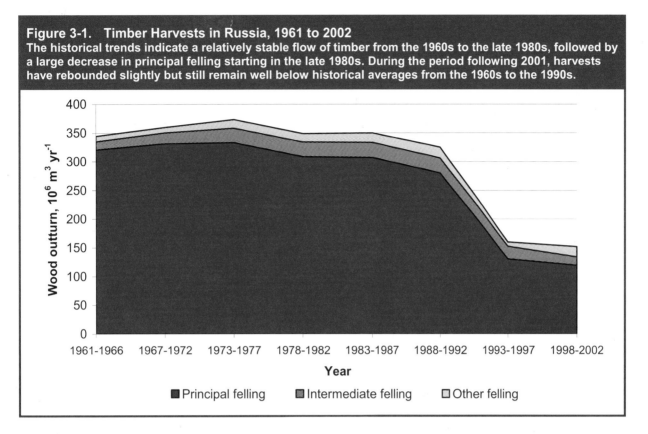

Figure 3-1. Timber Harvests in Russia, 1961 to 2002
The historical trends indicate a relatively stable flow of timber from the 1960s to the late 1980s, followed by a large decrease in principal felling starting in the late 1980s. During the period following 2001, harvests have rebounded slightly but still remain well below historical averages from the 1960s to the 1990s.

Forest Regeneration

Forest regeneration in Russia includes direct planting, seeding, and assisted regeneration (i.e., thinning to release more valuable trees) after harvest. This is also commonly, though not universally, referred to as "reforestation." Note that these reforestation efforts do not qualify under KP Article 3.3 but could be considered under KP Article 3.4 as part of forest management. Regeneration efforts have declined since 1990, from 1.8 to 1.0 million hectares per year (Pisarenko, Red'ko, and Merzlenko, 1992; Statistical Yearbook, 2000a, 2000b). The decreases followed the reduction in timber harvesting, as well as reductions in budgets. Despite these recent reductions, forest plantations occupy around 2 percent of the area of the SFFA, or around 15 million hectares. *Historically, forest plantations have been established at a rate of about 0.4 million hectares per year.*

In addition to traditional replanting efforts, some lands that have been affected by other extractive activity, such as mining, are reclaimed each year. Current estimates suggest that around 40,000 to 50,000 hectares of forestland are reclaimed each year. This represents a relatively large decline from the annual reclamation efforts (up to 90,000 hectares per year) accomplished in the early 1990s.

No separate estimates of carbon stocks or fluxes from replanting efforts are developed for this analysis. These forests are included as immature growing stocks in the SFFA inventory data and therefore are already counted in Tables 3-1 and 3-2 above.

Fires and Other Disturbances

Natural disturbances that influence forest area, age distributions, and carbon flux in Russia include fires, storms, harmful insect attacks, and other destructive processes. Forest fires remain the main cause of natural forest *mortality*, accounting for nearly 80 percent of the total area of natural stand death per year, or around 300,000 hectares per year on average since 1995. Insect and pest damage, followed by storm damage are the next largest categories, accounting for 13 percent and 7 percent of annual stand mortality, respectively, or an additional 77,000 hectares per year.

Forest Fire Trends. On average, 15,000 to 36,000 individual forest fires are reported on fire-protected lands in the SFFA. *Between 1990 and 2000, 1.1 million hectares burned per year on fire-protected areas, with the maximum area of 3.8 million hectares burned during 1998.* Since fire protection, and therefore monitoring of fires, only occurs on about two-thirds of the total forest area in Russia, these estimates likely understate the total fire occurrence and damage in Russia.

The great majority of fires do not kill all the trees that they affect. On average, for the years 1990 to 2000, about 25 percent of the trees burned in a given forest fire were actually killed by the fire. The larch forests of Eastern Siberia are relatively resistant to fire-related deaths, whereas pine forests that dominate Western Siberia have the highest rate of mortality per forest fire.

Carbon Emissions from Forest Fires. The volume of fire emissions estimated for the period 1990 to 2000 varies from 4 to 50 MTCE per year, with an average of 15 MTCE per year (Zamolodchikov et al., 2005). Most emissions (75 percent) result from ground fires. Post-fire mortality varied from 2 to 26 TCE per year over this period, averaging 11 TCE per year. Litter decomposition after a fire does not quickly translate into carbon emissions. Under stable conditions, however, its size will eventually be roughly equal to the size of total post-fire emissions. The sum total of fire and post-fire emissions from forest fund areas protected from fires is estimated at 26 MTCE per year on average for the period 1990 to 2000.

3.1.3 Wetlands

Data on the area and storage of carbon in Russia's wetland resource remain uncertain.

Different authors' estimates of the total area of wetlands vary substantially, from a low of 165 (Boch et al., 1994) to a high of 273 million hectares (Alexeyev and Birdsey, 1994 [in Russian] or 1998 [in English]). Similarly, the SFFA data have widely varying estimates of wetland area from period to period. This study relies on the SFFA data for 1998 and 2003 because these estimates of wetland area are close to each other and provide a consistent method of calculating wetland areas. Total wetland area is estimated with SFFA data to be around 132 million hectares (Table 3-3). Carbon storage in wetlands is estimated to be around 84.1 billion tonnes carbon, or around 637 tonnes carbon per hectare.

3.1.4 Agricultural Land

Land Trends in Agriculture. The total area of agricultural land in Russia has remained relatively constant in the past decade, although the total area of cultivated land fell from 118 to 85 million hectares (Figure 3-2). The decrease in cultivated land is due mainly to a decline in the area of grain crops, from 63 to 47 million hectares, and feed crops, from 45 to 30 million hectares. At the same time, the amount of area used for industrial crops (e.g., cotton, soy) and vegetable crops did not change substantially. In contrast, the area of fallow land has increased by around 24 million hectares. These areas potentially are in the initial stages of becoming forestland because agricultural land is abandoned in some regions. Most of this increase in fallow lands is occurring in the European part of Russia.

Table 3-3: **Carbon Stock Estimates in Wetlands for 1998 and 2003 Based on SFFA Estimates of Wetland Areas**

	1998	2003	Average
Wetland Area (Million Hectares)	132.6	130.5	131.5
Wetland Carbon Stock	BTCE		
Phytomass	0.9	0.9	0.9
Peat	83.9	82.5	83.2
Total wetland	84.8	83.5	84.1

Figure 3-2. Trends in the Structure of Agricultural Lands in the Russian Federation, 1990 to 2002
The total area of land classified officially as agriculture has remained relatively constant over the past 15 years. On that agricultural land, however, fewer hectares are devoted to crop production because some land has been allowed to remain fallow. The area in grazing and pastures has remained relatively constant.

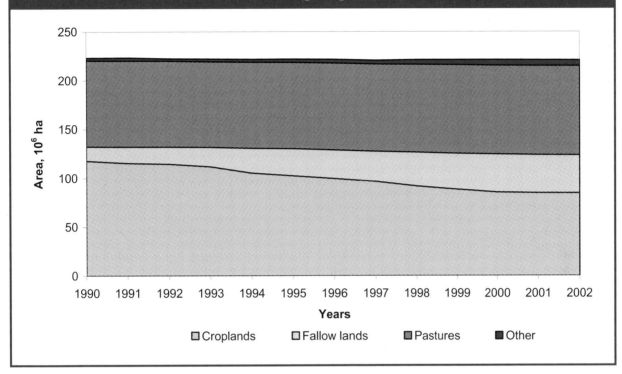

Carbon Storage on Agricultural Lands. Total estimated carbon storage in agricultural soils was 44.8 BTCE on average for the 1990s. These estimates are relatively constant, given that the total area of land in agriculture has remained relatively constant. Although the total pool of carbon in these soils is estimated to be stable, the area of fallow land has been increasing, and these areas potentially may be shifting to forest uses. Thus, carbon accumulation in these soils could increase in the future if these areas remain fallow and continue to establish forests.

3.1.5 Summary of Trends in Land Use and Forest Management in Russia

Agricultural and forested lands in Russia encompassed approximately 1.4 billion hectares during the period 1998 to 2003 (Table 3-4). Approximately 55 percent of this land is standing forest, 16 percent is agricultural (crop, fallow, or pasture), 9 percent is wetland, and 8 percent is nonforested areas that could potentially be forested. The remaining area, approximately 165 million hectares, is classified in the SFFA accounts as "other" and is generally

considered to be sites that are not productive enough to maintain forests, either because of soil types or climatic conditions (or both).

Data from the SFFA indicate that the forestland area has increased by around 0.3 percent per year since 1966. *Between 1993 and 2003, the area of forestland increased by around 1.3 million hectares per year, largely because of new forest growth on previous clear cuts, burned land, or other previously nonforested land in the SFFA accounts.*

Despite these increases, however, *there appear to be fairly large areas, potentially up to 107 million hectares, currently not forested but suitable for regeneration.* Some of this regeneration may be happening, but it has not been recorded yet in the SFFA data. Further, available data from SLA and other agricultural statistics suggest that an increasing area of land is left fallow every year. Between 1990 and 2002, approximately 2 million hectares per year were left fallow, increasing the total fallow area by 24 million hectares during that period. Evidence from comparing satellite-generated data of forest

Table 3-4: Land Area and Carbon Stock: Average of 1998 and 2003 Data

	Area	Carbon Stock (BTCE)[a]			
	Million Hectares	Phytomass	Soil	Total	TCE/ha
SFFA Forest Inventory					
Forests	775.2	34.0±5.0	125.6±29.2	159.6±34.2	205.9±44.2
Nonforested	107.3	0.8±0.1	18.0±4.5	18.8±4.6	175.2±43.1
Wetlands	131.5	0.9±0.2	83.2±24.1	84.1±24.2	639.5±184.4
Other[b]	164.8	0.4±0.1	26.4±8.6	26.8±8.7	162.6±52.9
Total SFFA	1,178.8	36.2±5.5	253.2±66.3	289.4±71.8	245.4±60.9
Agricultural Land					
Cropland	88.5	—	17.0±5.3	17.0±5.3	192.1±59.9
Fallow land	37	—	7.8±2.6	7.8±2.6	210.3±69.6
Pasture	90.6	—	18.9±6.2	18.9±6.2	208.6±68.8
Other	5.5	—	1.1±0.4	1.1±0.4	200.0±66.0
Total Agriculture	221.6	—	44.8±14.5	44.8±14.5	202.2±65.3
Total	1,400.4	36.2±5.5	298.0±80.8	334.1±86.3	238.6±61.6

[a] Average and 90 percent confidence intervals are provided for total stocks. The confidence intervals are based on standard error estimates of the initial means for conversion factors for biomass or soil stocks.

[b] Other land includes areas that cannot be forested because of low productivity.

cover to estimates of forest cover in the regions of Russia suggests that this land may be retired from agriculture and returned to forests. For the most part, these changes appear to be occurring in the European part of Russia, where most agricultural land is located.

Forest harvesting declined throughout the 1990s from 330 million m³ in 1990 to around 130 million m³ in 1998. Since then, harvesting has rebounded to around 150 to 160 million m³ per year. The area of forest fires averaged around 1.1 million hectares per year during the 1990s; however, this estimate accounts only for regions where forest fire activity is recorded. On approximately one-third of Russian forests no reporting is conducted. For the purposes of the estimates in this report, we assume that forest fires in these "unreported" regions double the total carbon emissions from forest fires estimated for the areas where reporting occurs. Regeneration efforts to rehabilitate forests with no or low stocking density declined sharply in the 1990s. In the early part of the decade, planting rates were around 1.8 million hectares per year, and

they have declined to around 1.0 million hectares per year.

3.1.6 Summary of Carbon Budget: Stock Changes

Across the 1.4 billion hectares in Russian forestland, agricultural land, and wetland, total carbon storage is estimated to be 334 (±86.3) BTCE, where the 90 percent confidence interval of estimated carbon is shown in parentheses. A large proportion, about 89 percent, of the carbon exists in soil components (Table 3-4). Phytomass in forests holds around 44 (±6.5) TCE per hectare, and soils hold an additional 162 (±37.6) TCE per hectare.

Estimates of the historical net flux of carbon are presented in Table 3-5, in addition to the carbon budget for Russia's forest ecosystems. Two alternative methods of calculating net flux are shown. First, net flux is calculated based on comparing the stock of carbon estimated for Russia's forested ecosystems between 1993 and 2003. This estimate is titled "Flux Estimated by Inference from SFFA Estimates" and is shown at the top of Table 3-5. Second, net flux is

Table 3-5: **Comparison of Potential Carbon Fluxes in Russia's Forested Ecosystems: Average Annual Estimate for 1993 to 2003[a]**

	MTCE per Year	Qualitative Uncertainty
Flux Estimated by Inference from SFFA Estimates		
Net flux (uptake) to forest biomass inferred from comparing 1993 and 2003 SFFA estimates of carbon in forested ecosystems[b]	40.0	Medium
Flux Estimated from Constituent Components		
Net flux from constituent components (sum of components below)	120.9	High
Forest growth (i.e., phytomass increment; uptake)	+238.8	Medium
Harvest emission	−56.3	Low
Fire emission		
In managed forest areas (detected)	−27.0	Low
In unmanaged forest areas (undetected)	−27.0	High
Emission due to other mortality	−7.6	Low

[a]Positive numbers indicate net uptake; negative numbers indicate net emissions.
[b]This estimate of net flux accounts only for forest biomass. It does not account for changes in debris and soil carbon pools.

estimated by adding up constituent components, including annual estimates of forest growth and annual estimates of harvesting, mortality and other factors that lead to emissions from forests. The net effect of accounting for these fluxes is shown as "Flux Estimated from Constituent Components" in Table 3-5. Qualitative estimates of uncertainty are provided, based on the authors' best guess.

Estimates of potential net flux during the period 1993 to 2003 range from about 40 to 120 MTCE per year, a net sink reflecting net uptake of carbon, using two alternative methods of calculating net flux. There are a number of reasons why this range is wide. First, a large proportion of the forest area was not measured within the 10-year timeframe considered, increasing the uncertainty around both estimates of flux. Furthermore, many forests are measured with aerial photography, so that total stock estimates may be inaccurately reported. Second, fire emissions may still be underestimated, although we have included an estimate of emissions from fires in regions where no reporting or fire-fighting activity occurs.

Third, it is not currently possible to estimate the potential flux of carbon occurring on fallow agricultural land that has not yet been classified as forest. A large proportion of these areas has only recently been left fallow and may be starting to accumulate carbon through natural

revegetation in forests or other plant material. The satellite imagery data indicate that much of the potential afforestation is occurring in the European region of Russia. Accounting for fluxes from early stage afforestation on fallow agricultural land would likely increase the net flux estimate.

As a result of the large harvests in the 1970s and 1980s, and the subsequent decrease in harvests in the 1990s, Russian forests currently appear to be a net sink for carbon. The proportion of young, fast-growing stands is at a historical high for Russia, at least within the measurement period of 1966 to 2003 used for this study (and likely for longer periods). These forests are entering their most rapid growth periods. In contrast, the proportion of mature and overmature stands, which typically do not accumulate as much carbon annually, is relatively low by historical stands.

3.2 Comparison of Carbon Budget to Other Estimates in the Literature

Table 3-6 presents a comparison of the estimates of carbon pools in forests and several important fluxes. *The estimate of the Russian carbon stock in phytomass in this study is 36.2 (±5.5) BTCE.* This estimate is well within the range of many of the studies conducted in the late 1980s

Table 3-6: Comparison of this Study to Selected Estimates from Other Studies of the Carbon Budget in Russia

Period of Estimation	Carbon Pool in Phytomass (BTCE)	Phytomass Increment (MTCE/yr)	Harvest Emission (MTCE/yr)	Fire Emission (MTCE/yr)	Source
1993–2003	36.2 (±5.5)	239	56	54	Present study
Selected Other Studies					
1988 (Former Soviet Union)	68.7	780	152	80	Kolchugina and Vinson, 1993
1988	35.6	243	85	31	Isaev et al., 1995
1988–1992	32.9	N/A	90	122	Nilsson et al., 2000
1998	30.6	N/A	65	16	Pisarenko et al., 2000
1998	32.7	N/A	47	19	Filipchuk and Moiseev, 2003
1990–1999	N/A	122	77	21	Gytarsky et al., 2002
1993–1995	39.6	N/A	56	N/A	Kauppi, 2003

and 1990s. Our estimates of the annual increase due to forest growth are most similar to those by Isaev et al. (1995). They are higher than Gytarsky et al. (2002) and lower than those of Kolchugina and Vinson (1993). The latter study included additional forests that were part of the former Soviet Union (now in other countries) and therefore should be higher in general. The harvest emissions calculated here are similar to those presented elsewhere. Studies that investigate later periods (after the early 1990s) tend to have lower harvest emission estimates because of the general decline in timber harvesting that occurred during that period. *The fire emission estimates vary widely among the studies: 16 to 122 MMTCE per year.* This is not surprising given the large uncertainties with fire areas and carbon emissions in the regions where forest fires are measured.

4. The Baseline: Future Projections of Land Use, Growing Stock, and Carbon Stocks in Russia

The baseline represents the business-as-usual conditions considered likely to arise without any direct policy

interventions intended to sequester carbon. A baseline projection reflects the expected influence of future land use change, timber harvesting, and management intensity in the Russian forestry sector. Development of a baseline helps researchers assess the potential to sequester additional carbon through policy action. All carbon that could be generated as a result of climate policy should be measured relative to the baseline to be considered additional to the baseline (see, for example, Forner [2002] and Watson et al. [2000], Chapter 5, for discussion of additionality).

The trends in forest stock conditions in this chapter are projected to adjust to demand for and harvesting of industrial timber, forest management, and land use. Future trends in forest fires and other natural disturbances, though possibly important, are not projected because reliable projection methods do not exist at this scale. Furthermore, the potential effects of future climate change on changes in the biophysical productivity of Russian forests are not included in the baseline estimates for this study. Several existing studies have examined future trends in forest management in Russia under assumed effects of climate change, but we ignore these potential changes to focus more directly on trends and carbon sequestration analysis.

For Russia, one issue associated with projecting future conditions is the definition of what is being projected and how it might be realized. Historically, government agencies in Russia have used the government's 5-year planning process to guide investment, production, and employment decisions. These plans establish objectives for production levels for the 5-year plan (and sometimes for longer periods). Before the 1990s, the plans were carried out with little consideration given to evolving economic conditions. In contrast, many landowners in market-oriented environments generate similar plans, but investment levels, production levels, and employment are determined by responses to evolving market conditions, not the plans *per se*.

More recently in Russia, resource allocation decisions have been more heavily influenced by market forces. Russia's transition from a centrally planned economy to one that includes widespread use of market approaches and economic incentives provides a challenge for making projections of land use and economic trends and for evaluating potential climate mitigation. For the purposes of this study, future projections of land use and management are developed with an economic model that assumes market forces guide all economic decisions (see Box 4-1). An alternative approach for several variables that develops future projections based on historical trend analysis and the planned activities by the Ministry of Natural Resources is described in Section 5.2.

4.1 Summary of Russian Experience Projecting Carbon Stocks

Several authors have examined future potential trends in carbon sequestration in Russian forests. These other studies indicate that over the next several decades roughly 150 to 330 MTCE per year could be sequestered in Russia in the baseline (Table 4-1). The studies include the carbon sink in all pools, including debris and soil carbon, and, as just discussed, some studies include climate-induced changes in forest productivity. Substantial increases in harvesting rates above recent historical levels could decrease the sink value by up to 50 MTCE per year (Izrael et al., 1997). In contrast, increasing fire protection has not been shown to

considerably alter sink estimates. In general, the model projections developed to date, and shown in Table 4-1, do not consider economic factors that could influence timber production (e.g., changes in global timber demand). The analysis in Section 4.2 below addresses this issue by using a global timber market model to assess potential baseline sequestration in Russia.

In contrast to the situation in Russia, estimates from Canada—similar in many ways to Russia in terms of climatological and forest resource conditions—suggest that Canada may become a net carbon source in the coming decades. Kurz and Apps (1999) indicate that for much of the 20th century, Canadian forests were a net carbon sink, but that this situation likely changed in the 1980s and 1990s, and Canadian ecosystems became a net source of up to 60 MTCE per year. However, forest products potentially have stored up to one-third of this emission, or around 20 MTCE per year in recent periods, according to the same authors (Kurz and Apps, 1999).

4.2 Baseline Harvest and Sequestration Projection Using a Global Timber Model

To assess the potential future sequestration or emissions of carbon from Russia's forests, this study uses the global timber model described in Sohngen et al. (1999) and Sohngen and Mendelsohn (2003) (see Box 4-1). To make the model more relevant to Russia, the data used and described in Sections 1 through 3 have been fully integrated into the model for this study. The global timber model is applied to develop a baseline of timber harvests, forest management intensity, species distribution, and land use change for Russia. The entire global market for industrial wood is modeled, but only the results for Russia are presented in this study. The baseline for Russia reflects projected timber harvest levels in response to domestic and global timber market demand and price levels. These harvests are used instead of the allowable cut levels included in Federal Forest Management Agency forest management plans, which are significantly higher potential harvest levels than those observed in the past decade in response to market forces.

Box 4-1:   Description of the Global Timber Model Used for this Study

The global timber model used in this analysis is built on the model originally described in Sedjo and Lyon (1990) and updated by Sohngen et al. (1999). The model has been widely used for policy analysis in recent years, including analysis of regional carbon sequestration baselines (Sohngen and Sedjo, 2000), climate change impacts (Sohngen et al., 2001), and carbon sequestration analysis (Sohngen and Mendelsohn, 2003). The model is a dynamic optimization model that maximizes the net present value of consumers' surplus less costs of managing, harvesting, and holding forests. The model is deterministic, so standard errors and/or confidence intervals over future forest conditions cannot be estimated. A global demand function for timber logs is used to estimate consumer surplus in timber markets. Forests in 250 timber supply regions then feed this global demand. Age class distributions for forests have been derived from local sources where available or assumed for regions without data on age classes. For temperate and boreal regions (most developed countries), age class distribution information has been obtained from local sources. Tropical forests are assumed to be in old growth conditions, while age class distributions for subtropical plantations have been derived from historical planting and harvesting rates.

For purposes of this study, substantial additional detail on the Russian forestry sector has been incorporated. Specifically, there are 108 timber supply regions assumed for Russia, based on the 2003 SFFA. These timber supply regions differ according to the following categories:

- Region: Europe, Western Siberia, Central Siberia, Far East
- Latitude: North, Central, South
- Timber type: coniferous, hardwood, soft hardwood
- Accessibility: accessible, remote

Age class distributions and timber biomass growth functions have been developed for each timber type. Cost functions for harvesting accessible and remote forests are developed from earlier estimates used in the study by Sohngen et al. (1999). Remote forests are those that have little infrastructure near them and consequently have high costs for timber extraction and transportation. These are based on costs for similar forests in different regions of the world. Since all prices and costs in the model are denominated by 2000 U.S. dollars ($), the relative costs for harvesting or accessing forests in Russia are adjusted for differences in exchange rates.

In addition to accounting for the costs of harvesting and accessing forests, land opportunity costs are modeled with land supply functions. The land supply functions represent land moving from nonforest use to forest use in response to an increase in the (rental) value of forest use. Land supply elasticity is assumed to be 0.25 for Russia (and for other regions in the model), indicating that a 1 percent increase in forestland rental values will increase forestland area by 0.25 percent at initial land rents and forestland areas.

Baseline projections of timber prices and timber harvests over the coming century are shown in Figure 4-1. Prices in the figure reflect those for U.S. softwood timber logs delivered to mills. Prices for wood in Russia (and all other regions) are indexed to this price and will differ only by wood quality, access costs, and transportation costs. Harvests are shown to decline over the century from current levels of around 145 million m³ per year in the coming decade to around 120 million m³ per year by 2105. The largest reductions occur in accessible regions. Remote forest harvests increase in the near term as growing stocks in those regions rise and harvests are induced by rising prices.

Forest area is projected to increase in the baseline (Figure 4-2) for several decades. During the period 2005 to 2015, forest area increases by an average of 907,000 hectares per year. This is somewhat lower than the implied afforestation rates over the past decade discussed in Section 3. Most afforestation occurs in the European portion of Russia, since this is where most agricultural land is currently located. Overall forest area in Russia is projected to increase by 14 million hectares over the next 50 years.

Table 4-1:   Examples of Baseline Future Projections of a Net Carbon Sink in Russian Forests from Other Studies

Source	Scenario Title	Net Carbon Sink, MTCE Per Year					Approach
		1990	2000	2010	2020	2040	
Izrael et al., 1997	Baseline forestry recovery	—	168	147	147	153	Simulations using CCBF (Carbon and Climate in Boreal Forests) model. Scenarios of forestry trends are used as input data. Account for forestry trends and warming influence from climate change.
	Intensive logging growth	—	168	144	131	101	
	Most intensive logging growth	—	161	104	97	40	
	Forest fire control	—	168	151	152	163	
	Baseline plus implementation of additional measures	—	168	160	172	207	
Lelyakin, Kokorin, and Nazarov, 1997	Baseline	—	217	276	334	—	Simulations using CCBF model. Scenarios of temperature, precipitation, and atmospheric CO_2 are used as input data. Capture increase of forest productivity due to warming and CO_2 fertilization.
	Minimal response to warming	—	—	191	—	—	
	Maximal response to warming	—	—	420	—	—	
Nilsson et al., 2000	Baseline with mean climate change	176	—	227	—	—	Use GIS data developed in IIASA FOR project. Scenarios are based on assumptions of future Russian GDP growth and current trends of productivity increase, induced by climate changes. Capture land use and forestry trends and climate-induced productivity increase.
	Low level of forest management	—	—	199	—	—	
	High level of forest management	—	—	248	—	—	
Izrael et al., 2002	Baseline	107	—	150	—	—	Simulations using CCBF model. Both forestry and climate change scenarios are used as input data.

Note that most of the studies include multiple scenarios, many of which are included in the table.

The influence of harvests, land use change, and timber growth on carbon stocks is shown in Figure 4-2. The estimates of carbon sequestration projected with the global timber model account for carbon stored in wood products, although these are a relatively small part of the total carbon pool and annual flux. Initially, forests in Central Siberia contain approximately 38 percent of forest carbon in Russia in 2005, followed by the Far East (30 percent), European Russia (22 percent), and Western Siberia (10 percent).

On net, Russian forests are projected to sequester approximately 70 MTCE per year over the decade 2005 to 2015. These increases are heavily influenced by changes in carbon stocks in the European part of Russia and Central Siberia, where current inventory information suggests that forest age classes are youngest (after heavy previous harvesting) and thereby growing faster. Annual storage becomes negative during the period 2025 to 2045, when harvests are projected to exceed growth during that period. Over the period 2005 to 2105, however, net sequestration is projected to be positive, increasing total storage by around 2.4 BTCE. This implies an average increase in carbon stored of around 24 MTCE per year over the century.

Figure 4-1.   Baseline Projections of Timber Prices and Harvests in Russia in the Global Timber Model Analysis

Global average forest prices are projected to increase slightly over the coming decade, although these increases are only 0.2 to 0.5 percent per year. Timber harvests in Russia are projected to remain relatively strong for several decades but to decline during the middle of the century. Most of the decrease occurs in accessible regions.

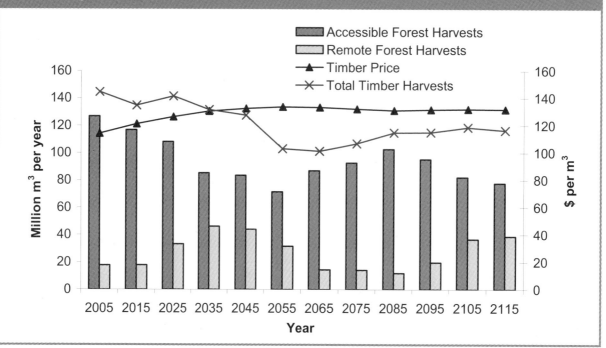

Figure 4-2.   Projected Baseline Annual Change in Forestland Area by Region in the Global Timber Model Analysis

Russia is anticipated to experience afforestation during much of the early part of this century, with most afforestation occurring in the European part of Russia. Most agricultural land that can support forests is located in this region of the country, and most of the change results from afforestation on old agricultural land.

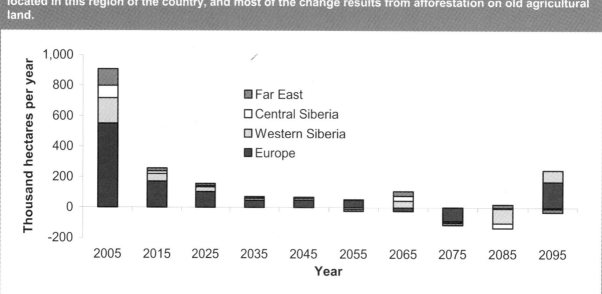

Carbon inventories, and the annual fluxes inferred from them are "net" numbers, balancing the influences of harvest removals and forest growth (on existing and newly afforested land). Ecological disturbances and other factors likely to affect carbon in forests, such as fires and pest infestations, for example, have not been modeled explicitly in this analysis. To the extent that forest fire areas and intensities increase over this same period, one would expect additional emissions, at least during the period when fires are most intense.

In addition to the baseline, it is important also to consider the possibility of stronger global demand for wood products, particularly given potentially strong economic growth in rapidly developing countries such as China and India. The baseline demand scenario used above assumes increasing demand for wood products (increasing 0.5 percent per year). A second baseline assuming stronger global demand growth, 2.0 percent per year, is consequently developed and used to estimate carbon sequestration. Stronger demand growth increases timber prices (1.5 percent increases per year initially) and increases harvests in Russian forests over the first several decades to more than 200 million m³ per year, with large additional flows from accessible and remote forests due to higher timber prices. The area of

timberland in Russia also increases by around 1 million hectares relative to the original baseline presented above by 2105.

Stronger demand growth over the century, however, reduces Russia's forest inventory, as more wood is removed and sent to markets. The carbon flows in the global timber model do account for long-term storage in wood products (30 percent of wood volume harvested), but this increased product storage does not offset losses from decay in the ecosystem. It is important to recognize, however, that the accounting rules for wood product storage continue to be debated in several international fora without resolution, including the UNFCCC. Projections of annual sequestration under the higher demand growth scenario are shown in Table 4-2. Stronger demand growth induces additional sequestration in the short term, but it reduces the long-term storage of carbon by about 1.4 BTCE relative to the baseline scenario.

In summary, these results indicate that under business as usual, annual carbon sequestration in Russia declines over the next several decades from the 40 to 120 MTCE currently sequestered per year. The results also suggest that substantially less carbon will be sequestered during the period 2000 to 2040 than the estimates from other studies reported in Table 4-1. A number of different factors potentially influence these

Table 4-2: **Annual Net Flux of Carbon Under the Baseline Case and the High-Demand Alternative Baseline Scenario in the Global Timber Model Analysis, for the Year Given**

Year	Baseline MTCE per Year	High-Demand Alternative Baseline MTCE per Year
2010	70.2	116.3
2020	20.1	11.6
2030	−30.5	−95.0
2040	−44.7	−135.7
2050	23.0	13.6
2060	63.9	73.9
2070	28.5	−1.7
2080	−6.7	−17.6
2090	44.3	52.6
2100	72.8	127.5

results. First, the global timber model uses growth functions for Russian forests derived from the current SFFA inventory. These growth functions likely imply less future growth than the earlier studies. Second, the harvesting decision is determined endogenously with timber prices (and not government plan projections), and this likely causes timber harvests to occur at earlier periods in harvested stands than those projected by the studies in Table 4-1. Third, many of the studies in Table 4-1 include the influence of potential global warming through increases in forest productivity. The analysis for this study with the global timber model assumes that climate change does not influence forest productivity in Russia.

5. Mitigation Analysis

In addition to assessing current trends in carbon fluxes in forests of the Russian Federation, a main objective (Question 3) of this report is to assess potential forestry actions that could be undertaken to increase the stock of carbon in forests in Russia. When accounting for forest carbon sequestration, it is important to distinguish between the technological potential and the economic potential (see Box 5-1). The technological potential describes the total carbon that could be sequestered under current or projected future technologies. The economic potential describes how much of this can be accomplished at different costs. In this study, we focus on estimating the *economic potential* for sequestering carbon in forests.

As noted in the introduction, the terms "bottom-up" and "top-down" are used to represent two classes of models used to calculate carbon sequestration costs. Bottom-up methods use detailed data on costs and carbon sequestration potential from individual projects and use that data to estimate the cost of engaging in those practices. Top-down methods, in contrast, use fairly aggregated data and modeling to estimate the marginal costs of carbon sequestration. Top-down methods typically use models that capture market processes by directly representing supply and demand. Both approaches have their advantages. Bottom-up studies rely on rich detail and site specifics, while top-down studies capture market feedback and opportunity costs that occur when land use changes and

Box 5-1: Comparison of Technological and Economic Potential for GHG Mitigation

When considering carbon storage potential, two estimates are relevant to consider for the purposes of this study.

Technological Potential (TP) for carbon sequestration estimates the biophysical potential for storing carbon in forests (ignoring economic and institutional factors). TP adds up the total area available for storage with the options that would produce the most carbon on that land. TP recognizes the inherent limitations of productivity on the landscape and uses these biological limitations to determine the maximum potential carbon storage.

Economic Potential (EP) for carbon sequestration incorporates the biophysical potential and both the direct costs and the opportunity costs of carbon sequestration (i.e., the opportunity to use land for alternative productive uses). EP recognizes that any actions to sequester carbon that result in *additional* carbon stored have costs. EP uses economic methods to account for these costs. Both methods used in this study represent options for estimating EP.

According to the IPCC (Metz et al., 2001), for any given price, or value, for carbon sequestration in forests, the following relationship between these two measures of potential exists: **EP ≤ TP.**

Previous studies have estimated the technological potential. In this study, we focus on the economic potential. We recognize that this will likely lead to less potential carbon sequestration than possible with current technologies; however, many of these technologies may be very expensive. In addition, there may be additional transaction costs that limit society's ability to achieve the lowest cost opportunities identified by studies, like this one, that estimate economic potential.

commodity production are affected. This study uses both bottom-up and-top down methods to generate estimates of carbon sequestration costs for the Russian forestry sector.

5.1 Options for Enhancing Forest Carbon Sinks in Russia

A number of different methods within forestry have been considered for sequestering carbon in forests in Russia.

5.1.1 Afforestation

Afforestation occurs when land currently used for agriculture or some other purpose is converted back to forests; definitions differ by country and for UNFCCC reporting purposes. On average for Russia, approximately 1.2 TCE per hectare per year can be stored when agricultural land is converted to forests. There are approximately 80 million hectares of agricultural land currently being cultivated within Russia, and while most will continue producing crops, it may be possible to convert some of this land back to forests.

5.1.2 Reforestation

Reforestation involves planting trees on sites that have been previously cut-over or burned; definitions differ by country and for UNFCCC reporting purposes. Poor harvesting practices, intense forest fires, or other factors often reduce the ability of forests to regenerate on some sites. Around 33 million hectares of forests in Russia have little to no stocking conditions because of previous harvesting or disturbance (Forest Account, 2003). In regions that are accessible, it may be possible to reestablish stands on these sites more quickly than would occur naturally and to speed up the accumulation of carbon.

5.1.3 Improved Forest Management

Improved management involves activities, such as thinning forests, to increase the ultimate accumulation of biomass on a site or to favor species with higher carbon densities or involves holding timber longer than current rotation periods to enhance long-term storage on a site.

5.1.4 Setting Aside Forests

Given large potential storage of carbon in above- and below-ground components of Russia's Far-East forests, maintaining carbon stocks on sites that would otherwise undergo harvesting could increase net sequestration. Some portions of these existing forests are likely to be harvested under future conditions and consequently generate carbon emissions. Set-asides provide carbon benefits by maintaining carbon stocks and avoiding the emissions associated with harvesting. Of course, such forests must also be protected from fires and other natural disturbances to maintain carbon benefits.

5.1.5 Reducing Forest Fires

Approximately 1.3 million hectares of forestland (in protected areas only) burn in Russia each year. Most of this burning occurs in regions where access is only possible by plane, and where determining that a fire is burning requires observation with satellites or airplanes. Reducing the number, intensity, or area over which forest fires occur could potentially reduce annual net carbon emissions in Russia, although carbon accounting for fire carbon fluxes over time is complex. Thus, activities that encourage early identification of fires and additional resources for fire-fighting equipment and personnel could help reduce the area of land that burns each year.

Assessment of carbon sequestration potential, and in particular the costs of carbon sequestration, requires consideration of several policy-relevant issues, especially whether it is additional to what would have occurred without a policy (additionality), whether the sequestration is permanent, and whether sequestration in one location causes emissions to shift to other locations (leakage). These issues are discussed widely in a number of other studies (i.e., Forner, 2002, Watson et al., 2000) and are not considered in detail here. With respect to the estimates of carbon sequestration costs presented in Sections 5.2 (bottom-up analysis) and 5.3 (top-down analysis) below, the bottom-up analysis accounts for additionality and permanence. It does not incorporate leakage. The top-down analysis accounts for all three factors, and the estimated costs are for permanent, additional carbon sequestered, net of leakage.

Box 5-2:   Carbon Sequestration Demonstration Project Experience in Russia

A number of GHG mitigation projects have been conducted in the Russian Federation to date, the majority of which have been related to industry and energy concerns (see Chapter 4 of technical report). Some of these have been targeted for eventual potential consideration as JI projects (Tangen et al., 2002). The expected reduction in GHG emissions from the various energy-related projects, assuming they are fully completed, ranges from 545 to 132,425 TCE. For forestry projects, those numbers range from 3,815 to 233,788 TCE. The cost of reducing carbon emissions by 1 TCE ranges from $13.58 to $167.00 for industry and energy-related projects and from $5.87 to $6.24 for forestry projects (Tangen et al., 2002).

One of the forestry projects, RUSAFOR-SAP, formally began in 1993–1994 in the Lysogorsky and Dergachevski Administrative Regions of Saratov Oblast (Kravtsov, Melochnikov, and Doronin, 2002; Vinson, Kulchugina, and Andrasko, 1996). The project represents a formal collaboration between the government of the Russian Federation and the U.S. Environmental Protection Agency and was approved by the U.S. Initiative on JI and reported under the UNFCCC Activities Implemented Jointly (AIJ) pilot program for JI (http://www.unfccc.int). Trees were planted in 1993 in the Lisogorski administrative region and in 1994 in Dergachevski. Monitoring has occurred every year of the project using 53 sample plots. The estimated carbon sequestered during the first 10 years of the Lisogorski project (1993 to 2003) was about 1.6 TCE per hectare per year and for the Dergachevski region about 0.4 TCE per hectare per year. For both projects, it is estimated that, on the 500 hectares of land planted, around 12,262 TCE will be sequestered over the life of the stands.

A more recent project in the Voronezh Oblast began in 1996. This project focused on planting forested shelter-belts through agro-forestry and has been carried out by the Russian Center for Environmental Politics (RCEP). This project is a prime example of collaboration between an environmental nongovernmental organization and local government in attempting to use potential future mechanisms for carbon trading. The project is estimated to sequester around 0.4 TCE per hectare per year, although these numbers have not yet been verified through measurement.

5.2   Bottom-Up Analysis of Mitigation Options in Land Use and Forest Sectors: Afforestation/Reforestation

This analysis focuses on four options for sequestering carbon:

1. *Improved natural reforestation* refers to areas that would regenerate naturally, but which would regenerate to higher stand densities more quickly with silvicultural assistance.

2. *Assisted natural forest regeneration* refers to areas that can only be reforested with additional silvicultural effort, such as planting trees.

3. *Establishing forest plantations* refers to afforestation in regions where substantially more productive forests can be established to increase overall productivity of the site.

4. *Protective afforestation* involves establishing forests in regions where substantial soil degradation has occurred and the forests can help rehabilitate the landscape.

The area of land available for options (1) through (3) above is derived from the 107 million hectares of unforested land in the SFFA. The pool of land available for reforestation amounts to approximately 33.3 million hectares of land. The remaining 74 million hectares are located in northern sparse forests and are generally not suitable for reforestation efforts.

The first three mitigation options are not equally feasible in all regions, because of land availability, ecosystem and soil characteristics, and previous land use history. Most of the available land is in the Asian part of Russia (94 percent), with 62 percent of the land needing reforestation occurring in northern regions, 32 percent in the central zone, and 6 percent in the southern zone (Figure 5-1). Of the total available land, 67 percent of the area (22.4 million hectares) is recognized as being able to support natural reforestation (option 1 above). The remaining 33 percent of these lands (10.9 million hectares) are classified as lands suitable for options (2) and (3).

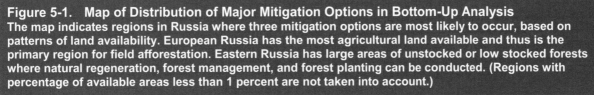

Figure 5-1. Map of Distribution of Major Mitigation Options in Bottom-Up Analysis
The map indicates regions in Russia where three mitigation options are most likely to occur, based on patterns of land availability. European Russia has the most agricultural land available and thus is the primary region for field afforestation. Eastern Russia has large areas of unstocked or low stocked forests where natural regeneration, forest management, and forest planting can be conducted. (Regions with percentage of available areas less than 1 percent are not taken into account.)

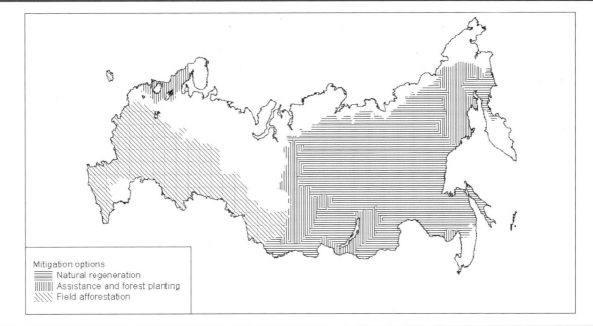

Mitigation options
≡≡ Natural regeneration
‖‖‖ Assistance and forest planting
⧄⧄ Field afforestation

One of the important institutional factors that make this type of reforestation possible in Russia is that the land is already classified as forestland in Russia. Therefore, no change in the legal status or intended use of these lands would be necessary. The more serious obstacle to reforesting these lands, however, is the lack of infrastructure in large portions of the Forest Fund that is oriented towards making reforestation measures possible. This is particularly important because much of the land needing reforestation assistance is located in eastern Russia, where there is less infrastructure development and forest access is limited.

The fourth mitigation option assessed, *protective afforestation*, includes land not part of the SFFA but intended to be used for establishing forest rings or water-side plantations for field, river, or reservoir protection purposes or for planting protective stands on steep slopes, sandy areas, or pastures. The Federal Objective "Increasing Soil Fertility in Russia in 2002–05" (The Government of the Russian Federation, 2001) reports that the total

area available for *protective afforestation* is 10.5 million hectares, the majority of which (94 percent) is in the European part of Russia, exclusively in the southern latitudinal zone.

5.2.1 Carbon Sequestration in Potential Afforestation/Reforestation

Average annual additional carbon sequestration across the four potential activities is estimated to be 0.58 TCE per hectare per year (Table 5-1). Sites in southern Russia, not surprisingly, are the most productive, as well as sites in the European part of Russia. Annual carbon accumulation rates range from more than 1.6 to 2.0 TCE per hectare per year in the southern zones of European Russia, to less than 0.8 to 1.2 TCE carbon per hectare per year in the northern zones of Eastern Siberia.

Note that each of the activities described above is occurring, to some extent, in the baseline, although current data suggest that the annual rates (in hectares per year) of accomplishing these four activities have declined in recent years. For this analysis, we

Table 5-1: **Reforestation and Afforestation Mitigation Option Potential in Russia: Bottom-Up Analysis for 2005 to 2085**

	Total Area (Million hectares)	Annual Area of Activity Undertaken (2005–2025) (Million hectares/year)	Additional Carbon Sequestration Over Baseline					
			Avg. Carbon Store by 2085 (TCE per hectare)	Avg. Annual Sequestra-tion (TCE per hectare)	Cumulative Carbon by 2015 (MTCE)	Cumulative Carbon by 2025 (MTCE)	Cumulative Carbon by 2085 (MTCE)
1. Improved natural reforestation	22.4	1.1	14.2	0.18	10.7	42.6	316.8
2. Assisted natural forest regeneration	9.3	0.5	29.5	0.37	30.9	109.7	275.2
3. Establishing forest plantations	1.8	0.1	86.4	1.08	12.2	30.5	152.2
4. Protective afforestation	10.5	0.5	120.1	1.50	21.8	162.1	1,297.1
Total	44	2.2	46.3	0.58	75.6	344.9	2,041.3

assume that the available areas today are completely treated over the next 20 years, beginning in 2005, as shown in Table 5-1. The baseline and *additional* carbon sequestered with each activity, then, is calculated based on assumptions about the increase in carbon sequestration that would occur (Table 5-1). The technical report (Zamolodchikov et al., 2005) provides more detail on how *additional* carbon sequestration is estimated for each of these options. No carbon price is used in the bottom-up analysis; instead, we estimate the costs of accomplishing the carbon mitigation quantity goal with the activities included in the analysis. Also note that we do not specify how such a program would be administered, by what agency or private-sector entities, or how the economic incentives would be generated and distributed to land owners or other institutions.

Annual additional carbon sequestration ranges from 23 MTCE per year by 2015 (year 10 of the potential program), 37 MTCE per year by 2025, and then a gradual decrease in yearly carbon deposits, for an average of 25 MTCE per year over the entire 80-year period. In total, 2 BTCE of additional carbon could be stored, increasing the net stock of carbon in Russian forests by around 6 percent above the current estimates of 34 BTCE.

5.2.2 Costs of Mitigation Activities

To estimate the costs of the mitigation activities discussed above, one must first determine the costs of the individual activities, such as assistance to planting, planting trees, and thinning. For this, the results from the Ministry of Natural Resources SFFA account on the execution of the forest management plans are used. An exchange rate of 28.5 Russian rubles to the U.S. dollar is used for the analysis.

Many of the costs of these projects occur before carbon is stored. To account for the time value of money, we use present value techniques to "discount" both the stream of costs and the stream of carbon arising from these projects. This allows the carbon sequestration cost estimates to be compared appropriately to other opportunities to sequester carbon, such as improving energy efficiency, geological storage of carbon emissions, and soil carbon sequestration. Table 5-2 presents both the undiscounted and the discounted carbon and cost estimates. The results show that 2 BTCE of undiscounted carbon can be sequestered over the next 80 years, or 25 MTCE per year with these methods. Undiscounted annual costs are $151 million per year, or $5.90 per TCE.

Table 5-2:   Cost Estimates (Undiscounted and Discounted)

Fund	Undiscounted			5 Percent Discount Rate		
	Expenses, Million U.S. $	Cumulative Carbon to 2085, MTCE	Carbon Cost, $/TCE	Expenses, Million U.S. $	Cumulative Carbon to 2085, MTCE	Carbon Cost, $/TCE
Improved natural reforestation	5,222.6	316.8	16.50	1,025.4	55.8	18.40
Assisted natural forest regeneration	2,227.7	275.2	8.10	513.9	90.9	5.70
Establishing forest plantations	608.7	152.2	4.00	268.4	32.4	8.30
Protective afforestation	4,005.2	1,297.1	3.10	1,187.3	223.6	5.30
Total	12,064.2	2,041.3	5.90	2,995.1	402.8	7.40
Note that estimates of cumulative gains by 2015, 2025, and 2085 are shown in Table 5-1.						

Under the discounted methods, the present value of the stored carbon is estimated to be 403 MTCE, and the discounted cost is estimated to be $3.0 billion, for a cost of $7.40 per TCE. The discounted costs are generally higher than the undiscounted costs because the activities to sequester carbon—and their costs—occur earlier than the carbon gains. In addition to considering the present value of carbon and costs, it is possible to put these values into annual equivalent terms. The annual equivalent carbon sequestration is 21 MTCE per year, and the annual equivalent costs are $152 million per year. These are both similar to the undiscounted average annual carbon sequestration and costs.

5.3   A Top-Down Approach for Estimating Sequestration in Russia

The analysis in Section 5.2 suggests that substantial carbon can be stored in Russian forests for fairly low costs. However, the methods do not account for opportunity costs that might occur under larger programs. Opportunity costs reflect the foregone value associated with producing other crops or outputs from the same land used for forestry activities. These are important costs of allocating land to forestry for sequestration and should be considered when estimating carbon sequestration costs. They specifically apply only to land that is considered "additional" (i.e., hectares added). Some land in crops in Russia is

currently shifting from agriculture to forests. Land that will be converted to forest because of current economic conditions (or projected future conditions in the absence of carbon policy) would be considered part of the baseline and would not produce additional carbon and by definition has no opportunity cost. Only agricultural land converted to forest above and beyond the baseline lands has opportunity costs in that it would otherwise be producing crops.

These opportunity costs must be estimated to get a full accounting of the costs of sequestration. To account for such opportunity costs, and to assess potential price changes that might arise from sequestration projects, a top-down approach for estimating carbon sequestration costs in Russia was undertaken specifically for this report, using the global timber model described in Section 4. The top-down analysis allows for the following activities: afforestation; enhanced forest management, including regeneration management and thinning; setting aside of remote forests from timber harvests; and storage in timber markets. Additional detail on the analysis can be found in the technical report (Zamolodchikov et al., 2005).

The analysis develops a set of scenarios that assume constant carbon prices over time ($5, $10, $20, $50, $100, $200, $500, and $800 per TCE). These prices broadly represent the range of potential prices generated by large-scale energy models used to estimate the costs of climate change policy. At the lower end, they also encompass current prices observed in markets, namely the $25 to $30 per T CO₂, or around $90 to $110 per TCE (as of September 2005) observed at the European Trading System.

The results indicate that for modest carbon prices ranging from $5 to $20 per TCE, an additional 3 to 5 BTCE can be stored by 2105. For these prices, the area of forestland expands by 2 to 10 million hectares by 2105. For higher prices ranging from $50 to $200 per TCE, an additional 8 to 20 BTCE can be stored by 2105, and an additional 30 to 125 million hectares of forestland are added in Russia.

A marginal cost function for carbon sequestration in Russia can be developed from these results (Figure 5-2). Quantities for the marginal cost function are given in annual equivalent carbon sequestration. This value is derived from the cumulative sequestration estimates by first calculating the present value of annual carbon gains over the century (2005 to 2105) using the 5 percent discount rate used in the model. With this present value of carbon storage estimate, the annual amount of carbon sequestration that would have a present value equal to this amount is calculated using the same interest rate. The marginal cost functions plot the carbon prices and the annual equivalent carbon possible under the alternative carbon price scenarios.

The results show that it is possible to sequester up to about 130 MTCE per year in Russia for up to $100 per TCE. Most opportunities to sequester carbon in forests in Russia are exhausted by $500 per TCE, or around 325 MTCE per year, as the marginal cost curve becomes very steep past this price. *The largest proportion of carbon storage occurs in the European region of Russia, and additional opportunities for carbon sequestration are exhausted at relatively low carbon prices in Siberia and the Far East.*

The global timber model allows us to compare marginal costs for Russia relative to several other regions, as shown in Figure 5-3. *As a proportion of total global carbon sequestration for $5 to $10 per TCE, Russia accounts for more than 18 percent of total sequestration.* Russia has mitigation potential similar to the United States and Europe for carbon prices below $200 per TCE. More carbon sequestration is possible in the United States for higher prices because more agricultural land is available in that country,

whereas most suitable land in Russia already is in forests. Europe has less total land area than both the United States and Russia and therefore has less mitigation potential. None of these regions compare to South America, where substantial sequestration potential exists because of large projected areas of deforestation in the baseline. For higher prices, however, Russia accounts for around 9 to 10 percent of total global sequestration potential.

5.4 Discussion of Carbon Sequestration Estimates

It is difficult to compare estimates of carbon sequestration across studies because different authors use different methods and consider different types of carbon sequestration opportunities. Some authors discount future carbon relative to present carbon, while others present undiscounted flows in different periods or cumulative carbon sequestered by a given year. Published studies rarely include enough data to fully compare across studies using consistent discount rates, project time periods, land areas, or sequestration alternatives. Although there is no universally accepted methodology, several enlightening comparisons across the results in this study and across the results in other studies can be made.

The first comparison we make is across the bottom-up and top-down results presented in this study. We have used consistent assumptions about discount rates in those studies, and they include similar sequestration alternatives, so they can be compared directly. The main difference in the studies described in Sections 5.2 and 5.3 is scale. The bottom-up analysis in Section 5.2 considered a single program encompassing a specific set of hectares that would sequester 2 BTCE by 2085. The top-down study in Section 5.3 considered a wider range of programs that would sequester from 2 to 48 BTCE by 2105. For comparison purposes, we use the smallest of the sequestration programs in the top-down study and compare that directly to the bottom-up analysis. For the comparison, we standardize the results based on the size of the program, using annual equivalent carbon storage potential over 80 years (2005 to 2085) suggested in the bottom-up results as the standard (i.e., 20.6 MTCE per year sequestered) (Table 5-3).

Figure 5-2. **Marginal Cost of Forest Carbon Sequestration in Russia: Top-Down Analysis Using the Global Timber Model**

The economic limit of carbon sequestration in Russia is estimated to be around 350 MTCE per year over the century for $500 to $800 per tonne. European Russia could supply the largest proportion of this carbon because of the large potential for afforestation. The other regions of Russia could supply roughly equal amounts at different prices.

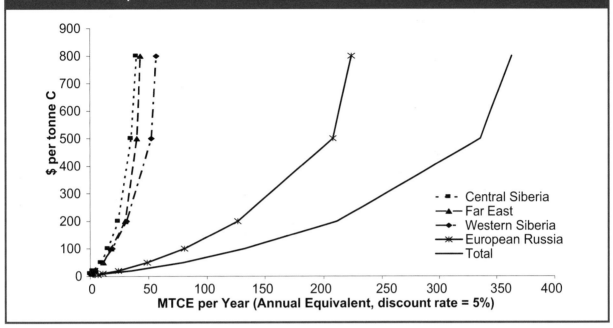

Figure 5-3. **Marginal Costs of Forest Mitigation Options in Russia Compared to Other Global Regions: Results from Analysis with the Global Timber Model**

For carbon prices ranging from $5 to $100 per TCE, the marginal costs in Russia are consistent with other temperate and boreal regions. For the entire range of prices, costs in Russia are fairly high and consistent with costs in Europe; however, the United States has relatively lower costs due to larger land supply from agriculture. South America, with large expected deforestation and high carbon storage potential, has substantially lower mitigation costs and higher economic potential than all other regions in this model.

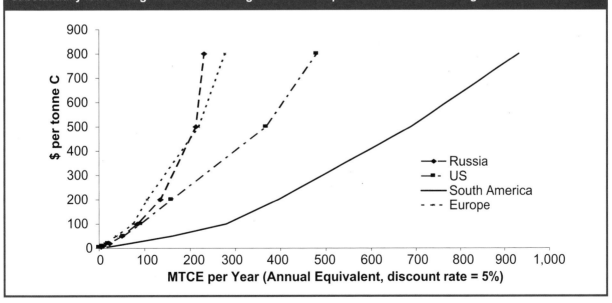

Table 5-3: **Comparison of Carbon Sequestration Potential Across Bottom-Up and Top-Down Studies Used in this Analysis for Comparable, Low Carbon Sequestration Costs**

Study Approach	Annual Equivalent Carbon Storage (2005 to 2085) (MTCE/year)	Cumulative Storage by 2085 (BTCE)	Cost ($/TCE)	Additional Forestland Hectares (Million hectares)
Bottom up[a]	20.6	2.0	$7.40	12.3
Top down	20.6	3.4	$13.18	4.3

[a]Carbon for all four alternatives is counted in the bottom-up results shown in this table, and average costs are presented. However, only the additional hectares in options 3 and 4 are shown in the fourth column because these are deemed to be additional land added to forestry. Options 1 and 2 are improved management techniques for existing forestland.

The bottom-up results imply that the average costs of this size program are approximately $7.40 per TCE, that 2.0 BTCE can be stored by 2085, and that 12.3 million additional hectares would need to be used for forests. The top-down results, on the other hand, suggest that the cost would be higher, $13.18 per TCE, but that cumulative storage by 2085 would also be higher, 3.4 BTCE. Fewer additional hectares would be used in the top-down study. The bottom-up study suggests lower costs in general because it assumes that more carbon is available in early periods, it assumes that there are no opportunity costs associated with planting additional forestland, and because it does not capture market feedbacks, it does not account for leakage. Accounting for opportunity costs and leakage increases overall cost estimates. Despite the differences in the bottom-up and top-down results, *our results indicate that about 20 MTCE annual equivalent carbon could be sequestered for less than $13 per TCE in Russia over the next 80 years.*

The second comparison we make is between the bottom-up results in Section 5.2 of this study and the results of a different bottom-up study by Shvidenko, Nilsson, and Roshkov (1997). That study unfortunately did not consider costs, so we cannot compare across costs. The Shvidenko study, however, did examine a number of forestry options similar to those in this study. The results of the comparison are presented in Table 5-4.

The differences in total potential carbon sequestered in the two studies are striking. There are a number of explanations for these differences. First, Shvidenko considers a substantially larger overall program (i.e., 189 million hectares in Shvidenko versus 44 million

hectares in this study). It is therefore no surprise that their study finds more carbon sequestration. Second, they assume a "zero" baseline for all reforestation-related options. Thus, all carbon on each site is assumed to be additional and therefore part of the carbon sequestration program. Finally, the estimates in this study are limited only to carbon pools in living phytomass, whereas all carbon pools are counted in Shvidenko. For example, the Shvidenko study assumes that 129.6 TCE per hectare is possible, while our results assume that only 45.5 TCE per hectare are possible.

The effects of these differences can be assessed by comparing the two mitigation options from this study, natural reforestation and assisted natural forest regeneration, with the Shvidenko estimation for reforestation of disturbed areas and reconstruction of low-stocked forests. The results in this study use 31.6 million hectares and generate 0.6 BTCE of additional carbon benefits. The results in Shvidenko use 80 million hectares and produce 12.9 BTCE, roughly 2.5 times as many hectares as our study and 21 times as much carbon. Similarly, the forest plantations and protective afforestation options in this study use 11.9 million hectares and produce 1.45 BTCE, while the Shvidenko options of reforestation in unforested areas use 64 million hectares (6 times as much) and generate 9.8 BTCE (6 times as much).

The third comparison we make, in Table 5-5, is to assess the economic feasibility of the large sequestration program suggested by Shvidenko. Their results suggest that it is possible to sequester substantial carbon (24.5 BTCE) over 100 years. Shvidenko does not provide a cost estimate. The results from the global timber

Table 5-4: Comparison of Biophysical Potential of Different Mitigation Options for the Bottom-Up Mitigation Analysis in this Document and a Recent Study that Examined Similar Options[a]

Option	Area Available (Million ha)	Additional Carbon	
		BTCE	TCE/ha
This Study: Bottom-Up Analysis, 2005 to 2085			
Natural reforestation	22.2	0.32	14.4
Assisted natural forest regeneration	9.3	0.28	30.1
Forest plantation	1.8	0.15	83.3
Protective afforestation	10.1	1.30	128.7
TOTAL	44.0	2.0	45.5[b]
Shvidenko, Nilsson, and Roshkov (1997): 100-Year Analysis			
Reforestation in unforested areas	64	9.8	153.1
Reforestation of disturbed areas	20	3.1	155.0
Reconstruction of low stocked forests	60	6.7	111.7
Rehabilitation of "climax" stands	20	2.2	110.0
Replacement of soft deciduous stands	25	2.7	108.0
TOTAL	189	24.5	129.6[b]

[a]Only the bottom-up analysis of this study and Shvidenko are included, since their mitigation options are similar and can be roughly compared.
[b]Average value of all options for TCE/ha.
Source: Shvidenko, Nilsson, and Roshkov (1997).

Table 5-5: Comparison of Carbon Sequestration Estimates and Costs in Shvidenko, Nilsson, and Roshkov (1997) Analysis and Global Timber Model Analysis in Section 5.3

	Tons Stored by 2100 (BTCE)	Cost ($/TCE)
Shvidenko, Nilsson, and Roshkov (1997)	24.5	Not assessed
This study (§ 5.3)	24.0	$290

model analysis indicate that 24 BTCE could be sequestered by the beginning of the next century (2105) for $290 per TCE. From a purely biophysical perspective, the results in Shvidenko are possible; however, economic analysis indicates that this much sequestration would be very costly to obtain.

The final comparison we make is to assess the scenario analysis conducted by Izrael et al. (1997). Their baseline for the next 40 years, guided by forest management plans, indicates that baseline annual carbon sequestration would be roughly 150 MTCE per year. They analyzed several scenarios, including increased forest harvesting and reduced forest fires. Under the increased forest harvesting scenario, harvests

would rise by around 50 percent over the next 40 years. This could reduce the estimated net sink in Russian forests in 2040 from 150 MTCE per year to potentially less than 40 MTCE.

The results in Izrael et al. (1997) show a similar directional effect of increased timber harvests on carbon sequestration as our high-demand scenario using the global timber model. However, the global timber model analysis suggests potentially larger reductions in net sequestration in the baseline over the next 40 years. Reductions in forest fire area (linear decrease of more than 50 percent over 40 years) would have the opposite effect of increasing carbon sequestration results by 2040, but only marginally. We have not analyzed carbon sequestration associated with reducing forest fires in this study.

6. Conclusions and Recommendations

The objectives of this report are to answer three critical questions related to measuring, monitoring, and managing carbon stocks and fluxes in Russia. From the analysis and application of the available data to several policy-relevant questions we conclude that Russia has substantial data available for estimating forest carbon-related variables, although improvements can and should be made over time. Each of the three questions is answered below.

6.1 What Is the Status of Russian Forestry Data for Assessing Carbon Stocks and Flows and for Conducting Analysis of Carbon Sequestration Potential?

Overall, data sources on forest inventories in Russia are available for use within the Russian-speaking community. These data are less readily available for the international community. The technical report upon which this study is based presents the data in substantial detail and provides a close review and analysis of the data for the international science community. Efforts should continue to make the data more available to scientists from around the world, such as by publishing the data on the Internet.

The scientific community in Russia has produced numerous reports over the years that provide forest stock, wetland, and agricultural area estimates for use in calculating carbon densities in forests, wetlands, and agricultural lands, and consequently carbon stocks. These methodologies follow international standards and protocols. Current Russian practices already conform to international standards.

Despite the general adequacy of data sources for producing carbon stock and flux estimates for Russia, a number of significant limitations exist that could be addressed through enhanced data collection and management. These issues and limitations are summarized as follows:

- *Recently, leskhozes have been required to provide information for the SFFA annually. This should continue if resources can be deployed to do so.* The aggregate forest inventory for Russia is compiled every 1 year, but detailed SFFA data are published publicly every 5 years. Increasing the frequency of publishing the forestry data publicly, perhaps every year, would enhance the ability of the research community to review changes occurring in Russian forests and carbon stocks.

- *In the near term, Russia should consider enhancing existing inventory methods to include collection of additional variables.* Current inventory methods were developed for, and are focused on, collecting data for forest management planning. While these data can be applied to estimate carbon stock and flux, observations on additional forest characteristics that are more directly tied to carbon storage would improve carbon estimates.

- *Forest inventory data should be collected more frequently.* In total, around 30 percent of Russia's forests have been inventoried with ground-based methods in the last 10 years. Inventories on an additional 32 percent of forestland inventoried with ground-based methods are between 10 and 50 years old. Photo-interpretation methods have been used on an additional 31 percent of forestland within the last 25 years, and the remaining 7 percent of forestland was last surveyed in the 1950s with aero-visual techniques.

- *Russia should consider developing and implementing a more systematic inventory system that optimizes resources to forest conditions.* In contrast to many other inventory methods, Russian inventory procedures call for collecting fewer variables on a larger proportion of the forest area. While it may be logistically and economically feasible to develop a network inventory system for regions currently using ground-based inventories, it is not likely possible to expand it to the entire country.

Russia should, however, consider developing a multiphase inventory consisting of remote sensing and systematic ground sampling, optimized by region for forest conditions (i.e., developing appropriate systematic procedures both for accessible and remote regions). In addition, Russia should consider using either ground-based inventories or photo-interpretation methods in regions where aero-visual techniques were last used.

- *Wetlands should be delineated according to a consistently applied standard.* Estimates of wetland inventories have been highly inconsistent, varying with the year the study was conducted and the parameters chosen by the researchers to define wetlands. Wetland estimates would become more consistent if the same standard were used consistently for all areas during many consecutive inventory periods.

- *The annual inventory of forest fires should be expanded to cover more regions.* Forest fires are recorded on only 67 percent of Russian forestland. Given the potentially large effect of forest fires on estimates of net carbon emissions or sequestration, particularly in regions where fire protection is not currently accomplished, it is important to inventory forest fire activity in these regions at least periodically.

6.2 What Is the Magnitude of Carbon Stocks on Lands in Russia Today, and Are These Stocks a Net Sink or Source of Emissions?

The results indicate that the Russian forest fund and wetlands currently sequester 36.2 (±5.5) BTCE in above-ground biomass and 289.4 (±71.8) BTCE in total when soils are considered. Agricultural land is estimated to store an additional 44.8 (±14.5) BTCE, for a total of 334.1 (±86.3) BTCE. The average carbon density on Russian forests is 44 (±6.5) TCE per hectare in phytomass and 162 (±37.6) TCE in soils. Average carbon density for wetlands in the forest fund is estimated to be 7.0 (±1.5) TCE per hectare in phytomass and 633

(±182.9) TCE per hectare in soils. Average carbon density for agricultural land is 202.2 (±65.3)TCE per hectare. On average, Russian forest fund, wetlands, and agricultural lands are estimated to contain 238.6 (±61.6) TCE per hectare.

Over the period 1993 to 2003, forests in Russia sequestered approximately 40 to 120 MTCE per year. This amounts to about 10 to 30 percent of annual carbon emissions from other sources (411 MTCE per year) in Russia (Secretariat of the UNFCCC, 2004). The lower-end estimate results from comparing carbon stocks across successive inventory periods from 1993 to 2003 (1993, 1998, and 2003). The higher-end estimate results from comparing individual fluxes derived from estimating carbon uptake in forest growth minus emissions from harvests, fires, and other mortality. Uptake from forest growth is estimated to be 239 MTCE per year. This is anticipated to decline in the future as the stock in younger forests matures and growth in these forests slows. Emissions from harvests are estimated to be 56 MTCE. These emissions declined sharply in the early to mid 1990s, although they have recently risen because of increased activity in the forest products industry. Fire emissions are estimated to be 54 MTCE. There is large uncertainty surrounding estimates of the area of forest that burns in Russia.

While we conclude that Russia currently is a net carbon sink in the range of 40 to 120 MTCE per year, we also conclude that there is a relatively large uncertainty band around this estimate, with the likely estimate residing near the lower end of this spectrum on average. The main uncertainties lie in estimates of stocks of forests in regions that have not been recently measured and in estimates of fire mortality in regions where fire protection is not conducted.

Analysis of future baseline sequestration using the global timber model indicates that forests in Russia are likely to continue storing carbon over the next 30 years, although net sequestration is projected to decline over time. These results are based primarily on economic drivers of harvesting activities. They do not consider estimates of potential forest fire emissions.

Our model's estimate of the net forest sink in 2010 is 70 MTCE per year. Russian forests are projected to become a net emissions source by 2030 as younger forests mature and harvest emissions exceed sequestration from growth. Over the entire century, however, Russian forests are projected to generate a net sink, growing at approximately 24 MTCE per year. Higher demand for timber over the century would increase the net sink capability of Russian forests in the short run, while reducing the long-term storage of carbon to 17 MTCE per year over the century.

6.3 What Is the Economic Potential to Sequester Additional Carbon on the Russian Forest Landscape as a Climate Mitigation Option?

The carbon mitigation analysis used both bottom-up and top-down methods. *The combined results indicate that it may be possible to store up to 3.4 BTCE cumulatively by 2085. Expressed on an annual basis, this is equivalent to additional storage of 20 MTCE per year (a discounted, annual equivalent amount) for relatively modest costs of less than $13 per TCE.* These costs are well below current prices observed on the European Trading System for emissions allowances, as of September 2005, but comparable to project-based emissions reduction costs. *Larger sequestration programs that would sequester up to 24 BTCE by the end of the century, such as suggested by Shvidenko, Nilsson, and Roshkov (1997) could cost as much as $290 per TCE.* Activities that focus on improving reforestation efforts account for a relatively small proportion of the total but would be concentrated mainly in Central Russia and the Far East. Activities that focus on afforestation would focus on the European region within Russia and predominately in the South.

The emergence of several prototype carbon sequestration projects undertaken in Russia starting in the 1990s suggests that Russia already has some early experience with mitigation projects. This experience could provide Russia with additional opportunities to mitigate carbon through additional activities, such as afforestation on agricultural land and enhanced management elsewhere.

6.4 Recommendations for Improving the Projection of Carbon Stocks and Potential for Mitigation in Russia

Recommendations to enhance Russia's ability to project carbon stocks in the baseline and to improve sequestration potential include the following:

- *Russia should continue to improve its ability to make projections of land use, land use change, forest stocks, and economic variables, given the potential importance of both industrial timber harvesting and natural disturbances.* Many studies that estimate future carbon fluxes in Russia focus on trend analysis and do not incorporate economic analysis or market feedbacks. Conversely, the economic analysis provided through the global timber model in this study incorporates economic modeling but does not explicitly account for natural disturbance processes. Improved projections would allow Russian ministries and analysts to evaluate alternative policies and agency plans and their GHG implications.

- *New estimates of opportunity costs of land uses based on Russian data and models are needed.* The economic analysis included in this study accounts for land opportunity costs but uses opportunity cost estimates for Russia imported from other regions with similar ecological characteristics. These models ideally should include the major land use sectors (e.g., forestry, agriculture, grazing lands) and a means to allocate land across competing uses based on the economic and institutional realities of Russia at a scale of resolution that provides adequate data for agency planning purposes.

- *Russia should encourage development of one or more case studies of carbon offset projects in the activities and regions considered most promising for large-scale mitigation.* While some experience exists to date in the RUSAFOR-SAP and Voronezh Oblast field afforestation (plantation) projects, additional experience in field activities, measurement, monitoring and reporting of carbon benefits, and institutional arrangements for establishing and implementing major sequestration opportunities would be instructive. In particular, significant opportunities for sequestration may exist in improved natural regeneration on marginally regenerating forest areas, assisted natural regeneration of harvest or fire-damaged forests, and perhaps fire management.

- *Russia should assess the need for government agency and oblast-level guidance to potential mitigation project developers* (landowners, nongovernment organizations, private companies, perhaps government agencies) to facilitate project development and the ability of projects to report carbon and other benefits and activities in ways that meet evolving or eventual government requirements.

6.5 Recommendations for Improving International Reporting of Land Use Change and Forestry

Recommendations to improve reporting of land use change and forestry for international agreements include the following:

- *Improve the ecological data collected in all regions and update inventory data in remote regions.* Current inventory methods focus on collecting data useful for industrial timber purposes. Although these data are adequate for calculating carbon sequestration, improved estimates could be made with revised inventory methods that focus on collecting data on a broader range of ecological indices. In addition, fairly large areas of forestland have not been recently inventoried, and it is important to verify estimates for those regions to increase overall certainty in annual carbon flux estimates.

- *Update forest fire flux calculations, in particular by enhancing data collection in remote areas where fire protection currently is not provided.* Emissions from recorded forest fires are

estimated to be 27 MTCE per year, or around 11 percent of annual forest growth. Emissions in regions where fires are not recorded, around one-third of total forestland area in Russia, could double this amount to 54 MTCE per year.

- *Compare ground-based data to results from satellite imagery.* The results in this study suggest that there currently is good correlation between recent satellite images and SFFA data. These comparisons should continue in the future and should provide information for ground-based inventory procedures. In addition, satellite imagery can assist with assessing forest fire emissions in unprotected areas.

- *Track area of agricultural land since 1990 and revise estimates of land use in forests on agricultural areas.* Satellite imagery and ground-based inventory do indicate that additional land controlled by the Ministry of Agriculture could be undergoing afforestation. Further quantification of these processes can improve the precision of carbon flux estimates.

- *Assess the need for a land use and carbon tracking system, including forest area, harvests, regeneration, afforestation, deforestation, forest fires, and other mortality.* Building a new carbon tracking system could aid in developing sequestration projects with domestic or international investors, and it could help the country meet KP obligations. If new forest inventory methods are developed and implemented to capture a wider array of ecological indices, these indices should be developed to feed directly into the tracking system.

- *Continue monitoring existing carbon sequestration demonstration projects.* Several such projects have been developed in Russia and indicate success in, and lessons for, implementing projects on the ground. These projects appear to provide quantifiable carbon sequestration and they should continue to be monitored.

Bibliography

Alexeyev, V.A. and R.A. Birdsey, eds. 1994. Uglerod v ekosistemakh lesov i bolot. [Carbon in Forest and Wetland Ecosystems]. Krasnoyarsk: Institute of Forest Science. In Russian.

Alexeyev, V.A. and R.A. Birdsey, eds. 1998. *Carbon Storage in Forests and Peatlands of Russia*. Gen. Tech. Rep. NE-244. Radnor, PA: U.S. Department of Agriculture, Forest Service, Northeastern Forest Experiment Station.

All Russian Research Institute of Silviculture and Mechanization of Forestry (ARISMF). 2003. "Russian Forests." Ministry of Natural Resources, State Forest Service. Published by ARISMF.

Bartalev, S.A., A.S. Belvard, and D.V. Ershov. 18–19 April 2002. "Novaya karta tipov zemnogo pokrova borealnykh sistem Evrazii po dannym SPOT 4-VEGETATION. [The New Land Cover Map of the Boreal Ecosystems in Eurasia Using SPOT 4-VEGETATION Data]." Aerokosmicheskiye metody i geounformatsionnyye tekhnologii v lesovedenii i lesnom khozyaystve: Doklady 3-ey Vserossiyskoy konferentsii, posvyashchennoy pamyati G.G. Samoylovicha. Moscow: Tsentr Ekologii i Produktivnosti Lesov. pp. 30–34. In Russian.

Bartalev, S.A., A.S. Belward, D.V., Ershov, and A.S. Isaev. 2003. "A New SPOT4-VEGETATION Derived Land Cover Map of Northern Eurasia." *International Journal of Remote Sensing* 24 (9): 1977–1982.

Bazdyrev, G.I., V.G. Loshakov, A.I. Puponin, et al. 2000. "Zemledeliye. [Agriculture]." Moscow: Kolos. 552 p. In Russian.

Boch, M.S., K.I., Kobak, T.P. Kolchugina, and T. Vinson. 1994. "Soderzhaniye i skorost' akkumulyatsii ugleroda v bolotakh byvshego SSSR. [Carbon Content and Accumulation Speed in Bogs of the Former USSR]." *Byulleten'* Moskovkogo Obshchestva ispytateley prirody 99(4): 59–69. In Russian.

Chestnykh, O.V., D.G. Zamolodchikov, and A.I. Utkin. 2004. "Obshchiye zapasy biologicheskogo ugleroda i azota v pochvakh lesnogo fonda Rosii. [General Storage of Biological Carbon and Nitrogen in Russian Forest Soils]." *Lesovedeniye* (2): 30–42. In Russian.

Chestnykh, O.V., D.G. Zamolodchikov, A.I. Utkin, and G.H. Korovin. 1999. "Raspredeleniye zapasov organichrskogo ugleroda v pochvakh lesov Rossii. [Distribution of Organic Carbon Storage in Forest Soils of Russia]." *Lesovedeniye* (2): 13–21. In Russian.

Dixon, R.K., S. Brown, R.A. Houghton, A.M. Solomon, M.C. Trexler, and J. Wisniewski. 1994. "Carbon Pools and Flux of Global Forest Ecosystems." *Science* 263(5144): 185–190.

Dyakonova K.V., L.I. Alexandrova, I.S. Kaurichev, A.D. Fokin., et al. 1984. Rekomendatsii dlya issledovaniya balansa i transformatsiya organicheskogo veshchestva pri selskokhozyaystvennom ispol'zovanii i intensivnom okul'turivanii pochv. [Recommendations for Exploring the Balance and Transformation of Organic Elements under Agricultural Use and Intensive Soil Cultivation]. Moscow: Pochvennyy institut imeni V.V. Dokuchaeva. In Russian.

Filipchuk, A.N. and B.N. Moiseev. 2003. "Vklad lesov Rossii v uglerodnyy balans planety. [Contribution of the Russian Forest to Carbon Balance of the Planet]." *Lesokhozyaystvennaya informatsiya* 1: 27–34. In Russian.

Filipchuk, A.N., V.V. Stakhov, V.A. Borisov, et al., eds. 2000. Kratkiy Natsional'nyy ocherk o sektore lesnogo khozyaystva i lesnykh tovarov: Rossiyskaya Federatsiya. [Brief National Overview of the Forest Management and Forest Products: the Russian Federation] New York, Geneva: United Nations. In Russian.

Forest Account. 2003. *Lesnoy fond Rossii (po uchetu na 1 yanvarya 2003 g.).* [Forest Fund of Russia (according to the account of 1 January 2003)]. Moscow: VNIITsLesresurs. In Russian.

Forest Account. 2004. *Lesnoy fond Rossii (po uchetu na 1 yanvarya 2004 g.).* [Forest Fund of Russia (according to the account of 1 January 2004)]. Moscow: VNIITsLesresurs. In Russian.

Forner, C. 2002. "LULUCF and Climate Change, A Field for Battles?" Unpublished manuscript by UNFCCC Secretariat, Bonn, Germany. Available from http://www.joanneum.ac.at/CarboInvent/workshop/Post 2012 workshop/background documents.

Gillis, M.D. 2001. "Canada's National Forest Inventory (Responding to Current Information Needs)." *Environmental Monitoring and Assessment* 67: 121–129.

The Government of the Russian Federation. 2001. Povysheniye plodorodiya pochv Rossii na 2002–2005. Federal'naya tselevaya programma, utverzhdennaya Pravitel'stvom Rossiyskoy Federatsii ot 8 noyabrya 2001 g. # 780. [Increasing Soil Fertility in Russia in 2002–2005. Federal Project Objective, Approved by the Government of the Russian Federation on 8 November 2001. # 780]. In Russian.

Gytarsky, M.L., R.T. Karaban, A.N. Filipchuk, V.N. Korotkov, and A.A. Romanovskaya. 2002. "Raschetnaya otsenka stoka ugleroda v lesakh Rossii za posledneye desyatiletiye. [Accounting Carbon Flow in Russia's Forests over the Past Decade]." *Raschetnaya otsenka stoka ugleroda v lesakh Rossii za posledneye desyatiletiye* V (XVIII): 216–275. In Russian.

Intergovernmental Panel on Climate Change (IPCC). 2003. Penman J., M. Gytarsky, T. Hiraishi, T. Krug, D. Kruger, R. Pipatti, L. Buendia, K. Miwa, T. Ngara, K. Tanabe, and F. Wagner, eds. "Good Practice Guidance for Land Use, Land Use Change and Forestry." IPCC/OECD/IEA/IGES, Hayama, Japan. Available from http://www.ipcc-nggip.iges.or.jp/public/gpglulucf/gpglulucf.htm.

Isaev, A.S., G.N. Korovin, V.I. Sukhikh, S.P. Titov, A.I. Utkin, A.A. Golub, D.G. Zamolodchikov, and A.A. Pryazhnikov. 1995. *"Ekologicheskiye problemy pogloshcheniya uglekislogo gaza posredstvom losovosstanovleniya i lesorazvedeniya v Rossii.* [Environmental Problems of Carbon Dioxide Sequestration through Afforestation and Reforestation in Russia]." Moscow: Tsentr ekologicheskoy politiki. In Russian.

Isaev, A.S., G.N. Korovin, A.I. Utkin, A.A. Pryazhnikov, and D.G. Zamolodchikov. 1993. "Otsenka zapasov i godichnogo deponirovaniya ugleroda v fitomasse lesnykh ekosistem Rossii. [Assessment of Carbon Storage and Yearly Deposit in Phytomass of the Russian Forest Ecosystems]." *Lesovedeniye* 5: 3–10. In Russian.

Izrael Yu. A., M.L. Gytarsky, R.T. Karaban, A.L. Lelyakin, and I.M. Nazarov. 2002. "Consequences of Climate Change for Forestry and Carbon Dioxide Sink in Russian Forests." *Izvestiya, Atmospheric and Oceanic Physics* 38 (Suppl. 1): S84–S98.

Izrael Yu. A., I.M. Nazarov, R.T. Karaban, A.L. Kljucharev, A.O. Kokorin, et al. 1997. "Russian Federation Climate Change Country Study." *Volume 4. Mitigation Analysis.* Moscow: Russian Federal Service for Hydrometeorology and Environmental Monitoring.

Kauppi, P.E. 2003. "New, Low Estimate for Carbon Stock in Global Forest Vegetation Based on Inventory Data." *Silvia fennica* 37(4): 451–457.

Kolchugina, T.P, and T.S. Vinson. 1993. "Equilibrium Analysis of Carbon Pools and Fluxes of Forest Biomes in the Former Soviet Union." *Canadian Journal of Forest Research* 23: 81–88.

Kononova, M.M. 1984. "Organicheskoye veshchestvo i plodorodiye pochv. [Organic Elements and Soil Fertility]." *Organicheskoye veshchestvo i plodorodiye pochv* 8: 6–20. In Russian.

Kravtsov, S.Z., A.S. Melochnikov, and K.M. Doronin. 2002. *"Desyat' let mezhdunarodnomu rossiysko-amerikanskomu proyektu RUSAFOR-SAP posozdaniyu novykh uglerodoyemkikh lesov v Saratovkoy oblasti.* [Ten Years of the International Russian-American Project RUSAFOR-SAP on Afforestation for Carbon Sequestration in the Saratov Region]." Saratov: SGTU. In Russian.

Kurz, W. and M. Apps. 1999. "A 70-Year Retrospective Analysis of Carbon Fluxes in the Canadian Forest Sector." *Ecological Applications* 9(2): 526–547.

Kurz, W. and M. Apps. 2005. "Developing Canada's National Forest Carbon Monitoring, Accounting and Reporting System to Meet the Reporting Requirements of the Kyoto Protocol." In press: *Mitigation and Adaptation Strategies for Global Change.*

Kurz, W., M. Apps, E. Banfield, and G. Stinson. 2002. "Forest Carbon Accounting at the Operational Scale." *The Forestry Chronicle* 78(5): 672–679 Available from http://www.joanneum.ac.at/CarboInvent/workshop/Post 2012 workshop/background documents.

Lelyakin, A.L., A.O. Kokorin, and I.M. Nazarov. 1997. "Vulnerability of Russian Forests to Climate Changes. Model Estimation of CO_2 Fluxes." *Climatic Change* (36): 123–133.

McCarthy, J.J., O.F. Canziani, N.A. Leary, D.J. Dokken, and K.S. White, eds. 2001. "Climate Change 2001: Impacts, Adaptation, and Vulnerability." Cambridge, UK: Cambridge University Press.

Metz, B., O. Davidson, R. Swart, and J. Pan. 2001. "Climate Change 2001: Mitigation." Cambridge, UK: Cambridge University Press.

Nilsson, S., A. Shvidenko, V. Stolbovoi, V. Gluck, J. Mattias, M. Obersteiner. 2000. "Full Carbon Account for Russia." *IIASA Interim Report.* Luxenburg, Austria: International Institute of Applied Analysis (IIAA). 1R-00-021.

Nordhaus, W., and J. Boyer. 2000. *Warming the World: Economic Models of Global Warming.* Cambridge, MA: MIT Press.

Orlov, D.S., O.N. Biryukova, and N.I. Sukhanova. 1996. *Organicheskoye veshchestvo pochv Rossiyskoy Federatsii.* [Organic Elements in Soils of the Russian Federation]. Moscow: Nauka. In Russian.

Pisarenko, A.M., G.I. Red'ko, and M.D. Merzlenko. 1992. *"Iskusstvennyye lesa.* [Artificial Forest]. Part I." Moscow: YuNIFIR, VNIITsLesresurs. In Russian.

Pisarenko, A.M., V.V. Strakhov, B.N. Moiseev, and A.M. Alferov. 2000. "Vklad lesov Rossii v uglerodnyy balans planety i problema lesovosstanovleniya. [Contribution of the Russian Forest to the Carbon Balance of the Planet and the Issue of Reforestation]." *Byulleten' Ispol'zovaniye i okhrana prirodnykh resursov Rossii* 6: 54–66. In Russian.

Secretariat of the UNFCCC. 2004. "Information on National Greenhouse Gas Inventory Data from Parties Included in Annex I to the Convention for the Period 1990–2002." Available from http://ghg.unfccc.int/index.html (FCCC/CP/2004/5).

Sedjo, R. and K. Lyon. 1990. *The Long-Term Adequacy of World Timber Supply.* Washington, DC: Resources for the Future.

Shvidenko A., S. Nilsson, and V. Roshkov. 1997. "Possibilities for Increased Carbon Sequestration through the Implementation of Rational Forest Management in Russia." *Water, Air and Soil Pollution* 94: 137–162.

Sohngen, B. and R. Mendelsohn. 2003. "An Optimal Control Model of Forest Carbon Sequestration." *American Journal of Agricultural Economics* 85(2): 448–457.

Sohngen, B., R. Mendelsohn, and R. Sedjo. 1999. "Forest Management, Conservation, and Global Timber Markets." *American Journal of Agricultural Economics* 81(1): 1–13.

Sohngen, B., R. Mendelsohn, and R. Sedjo. 2001. "A Global Model of Climate Change Impacts on Timber Markets." *Journal of Agricultural and Resource Economics* 26(2): 326–343.

Sohngen, B. and R. Sedjo. 2000. "Potential Carbon Flux from Timber Harvests and Management in the Context of a Global Timber Market." *Climatic Change* 44: 151–172.

Statistical Yearbook. 2000a. *Rossiyskiy statisticheskiy ezhegodnik.* [Russian Statistical Yearbook]. Moscow: Goskomstat. In Russian.

Statistical Yearbook. 2000b. *Sel'skoye khozyaystvo v Rossii.* [Agriculture in Russia]. Moscow: Goskomstat. In Russian.

Stolbovoi, V., and I. McCallum. 2002. The CD-ROM Land Resources of Russia. IIASA, Russian Academy of Sciences.

Tangen, K., A. Corpoo, V. Berdin, et al. 2002. "Tselevyye ekologicheskiye investitsii v Rossii. Mezhdunarodnaya torgovlya kvotami na vybrosy parnikovykh gazov kak instrument okhrany prirody. [Target Green Investments in Russia. International Emission Quota Trading for GreenHouse Gases as a Tool for Nature Protection]." Moscow: WWF. In Russian.

Tyurin, I.V. 1937. *"Organicheskoye veshchestvo pochv i yego rol' v pochvoobrazovanii i plodorodii: Ucheniye o pochvennom gumusye.* [Organic Element in Soils and Its Role in Soil Formation and Fertility: A Study on Soil Humus]." Moscow, Leningrad: Sel'khozgiz. In Russian.

Utkin, A.I. 2003. "Izucheniye pulov i potokov ugleroda na urovnyakh ekosistemy i territorial'nogo kompleksa. [A Study of Carbon Pool and Fluxes on Levels of Ecosystem and Territorial Complex]." Mezhdunarodnaya konferentsiya "Statsionarnyye lesoekologicheskiye issledovaniya: metody, itogi, perspektivy." [International Conference "Stationary Research in Forest Ecology: Methods, Results, Perspectives"]. 15–16 September 2003. Syktyvkar, Komi Republic. Syktyvkar: Biology Institute of Komi NTs URO RAN. pp. 9–13. In Russian.

Utkin, A.I., Y.I. Gul'be, T.A. Gul'be, and L.S. Ermolova. 1994. *Biologicheskaya produktivnost' lesnykh ekosistem. Komputernaya baza dannykh.* [Biological Productivity of Forest Ecosystems. Computer Database]." Moscow: IL RAN, TsEPL RAN. In Russian.

Utkin, A.I., D.G. Zamolodchikov, O.V. Chestnykh, G.N. Korovin, and N.V. Zukert. 2001. "Lesa Rossii kak rezervuar organicheskogo ugleroda biosfery. [Russian Forest as a Sink Tank for Biospheric Organic Carbon]." *Lesa Rossii kak rezervuar organicheskogo ugleroda biosfery* 5: 8–23. In Russian.

Utkin, A.I., D.G. Zamolodchikov, G.N. Korovin, and O.V. Chestnykh. 2002. "Reserves and Density of Organic Carbon in Forests of Russia." *The Role of Boreal Forests and Forestry in the Global Carbon Budget. Proceedings of IBFRA 2000 Conference.* May 8–12, 2000. Edmonton, Alberta, Canada. Edmonton: Canadian Forest Service. pp. 227–240.

Vinson, T.S., T.P. Kulchugina, and K. Andrasko. 1996. "Greenhouse Gas Mitigation Options in the Forest Sector of Russia: National and Project Level Assessments." *Environmental Management* 20 (Suppl 1): S111–18.

Watson, R.T., I.R. Noble, B. Bolin, N.H. Ravindranath, D.J. Verardo, and D.J. Dokken. 2000. *Land Use, Land-Use Change, and Forestry.* Cambridge, UK: Cambridge University Press.

Zamolodchikov, D.G., G.N. Korovin, A.I. Utkin, O.V. Chestnykh, and B. Sohngen. 2005. "Uglerod v lesnom fonde I selskokhozaistvennykh ugodyakh Rossii" [*Carbon in Forest and Agricultural Lands of Russia*]. KMK Scientific Press Ltd. 200 p. In Russian.

About the Authors

Brent Sohngen is a Senior Economist at RTI International in North Carolina, USA, and an Associate Professor in the Department of Agricultural, Environmental, and Development Economics at The Ohio State University, Columbus, Ohio, USA.

Kenneth Andrasko is a Senior Sequestration Expert in the Office of Air and Radiation/Climate Change Division at the U.S. Environmental Protection Agency in Washington, DC, USA. He was a co-founder of the RUSAFOR carbon sequestration project in Russia in the mid-1990s and has coauthored five UN IPCC reports.

Mikhail Gytarsky is a Senior Scientist at the Institute of Global Climate and Ecology of the Russian Federal Service for Hydrometeorology and Environmental Monitoring and Russian Academy of Science in Moscow, Russian Federation. He is a member of the national greenhouse gas inventory team and the author of the IPCC's "Good Practice Guidance for Land Use, Land Use Change and Forestry" and of the 2006 IPCC "Guidelines for National Greenhouse Gas Inventories."

George Korovin is Director of the Forest Ecology and Production Center of the Russian Academy of Sciences in Moscow. He is a well-known expert on the forest carbon cycle, forest fire impacts and protection, and mathematical modeling of forest dynamics.

Lars Laestadius, a Senior Associate at WRI, leads its forestry-related work in Russia. This work includes establishing partnerships, designing and facilitating forest information fora, mapping high conservation value forests, and assessing the impact of the oil industry on Russia's forest landscape.

Brian Murray is Director of the Center for Regulatory Economics and Policy Research at RTI International. He has worked extensively on the economic analysis of climate change mitigation strategies in forestry and agriculture and was a convening lead author of the IPCC "Special Report on Land Use, Land Use Change and Forestry."

Anatoly Utkin is a Leading Scientist at the Institute of Forest Science of the Russian Academy of Sciences in Uspenskoye, Russia. His scientific interests are forest productivity, forest carbon and other biogeochemical cycles, and forestry strategies.

Dmitry Zamolodchikov is Deputy Director of the Forest Ecology and Production Center of the Russian Academy of Sciences in Moscow. His scientific interests include the carbon cycle of arctic and temperate ecosystems, the influence of climatic changes on terrestrial ecosystems, system analysis, and mathematical modeling. He is also the lead author of the broader technical report on which this summary report is based (Zamolodchikov et al., 2005).

World Resources Institute

The World Resources Institute is an environmental think tank that goes beyond research to create practical ways to protect the Earth and improve people's lives. Our mission is to move human society to live in ways that protect Earth's environment for current and future generations.

Our program meets global challenges by using knowledge to catalyze public and private action:

- **To reverse damage to ecosystems**. We protect the capacity of ecosystems to sustain life and prosperity.

- **To expand participation in environmental decisions**. We collaborate with partners worldwide to increase people's access to information and influence decisions about natural resources.

- **To avert dangerous climate change**. We promote public and private action to ensure a safe climate and sound world economy.

- **To increase prosperity while improving the environment**. We challenge the private sector to grow by improving environmental and community well-being.

In all of our policy research and work with institutions, WRI tries to build bridges between ideas and actions, meshing the insights of scientific research, economic and institutional analyses, and practical experience with the need for open and participatory decision making.

Forest Ecology and Production Center

The Forest Ecology and Production Center (FEPC) of the Russian Academy of Sciences was founded in 1991. The main goal of the FEPC is coordination of scientific research in Russia and development of international scientific cooperation on issues related to forest ecology, forest monitoring, biodiversity, and environmental functions of forests. FEPC's primary areas of research are estimation of biospheric functions of Russian forests, forest monitoring using remote sensing and geographic information system (GIS) technologies, investigation of biological and structural diversity of forest ecosystems, biogeochemistry, and resistance.

RTI International[1]

RTI International is an independent not-for-profit organization dedicated to conducting innovative, multidisciplinary research that improves the human condition. With a worldwide staff of more than 2,500 people, RTI conducts research on a full spectrum of issues in economic and social development, the environment, health, advanced technology, survey and statistics, and education. Universities in North Carolina founded RTI in 1958 as the first scientific organization in and centerpiece of the Research Triangle Park.

---

[1] RTI International is the trade name of Research Triangle Institute.